Revision

Framework

MATHS

National Curriculum Levels 5-7

David Capewell

Jayne Kranat

Peter Mullarkey

OXFORD

UNIVERSITY PRESS

OXFORD
UNIVERSITY PRESS

Great Clarendon Street, Oxford OX2 6DP

Oxford University Press is a department of the University of Oxford.
It furthers the University's objective of excellence in research,
scholarship, and education by publishing worldwide in

Oxford New York

Auckland Cape Town Dar es Salaam Hong Kong Karachi
Kuala Lumpur Madrid Melbourne Mexico City Nairobi
New Delhi Shanghai Taipei Tokyo Toronto

With offices in

Argentina Austria Brazil Chile Czech Republic France Greece
Guatemala Hungary Italy Japan South Korea Poland Portugal
Singapore Switzerland Thailand Turkey Ukraine Vietnam

Oxford is a registered trade mark of Oxford University Press
in the UK and in certain other countries

British Library Cataloguing in Publication Data

Data available

ISBN 019 914944 5

10 9 8 7 6 5 4 3 2 1

Typeset by Mathematical Composition Setters Ltd.

Printed by Unigraph, Spain.

Acknowledgements
The publisher would like to thank QCA for their kind permission to use
Key Stage 3 test questions.

About this book

This book has been written to help you revise for the National Tests at the end of KS3 Mathematics and is aimed at the 5–7 tier of entry.

The books consists of three types of pages:
▷ Content pages that set out the information you need to know and provide practice
▷ Revision pages that consist of past paper test questions
▷ Practice test paper pages that provide confidence for the real thing.

The **Content** pages are organised into Number (N), Algebra (A), Shape, space and measures (S) and Data handling (D).

They tell you the main ideas you need to know and remember.

Key points tell you the information you need to know.

▶ To change a decimal to a percentage you multiply by 100.

$$0.375 = 37.5\% \qquad (0.375 \times 100 = 37.5)$$

Worked examples show the skills you need in the tests, and margin boxes give you extra hints and tips.

> **example**
>
> Find **a** $\frac{4}{27} \times \frac{6}{11}$ **b** 17% of 80 000.
>
> **a** $\frac{4}{{}_{9}\cancel{27}} \times \frac{\cancel{6}^{2}}{11} = \frac{4}{9} \times \frac{2}{11} = \frac{8}{99}$ **b** $\frac{17}{\cancel{100}} \times 80\,0\cancel{00} = 17 \times 800 = 13\,600$

You can change between fractions, decimals and percentages to make it easier to calculate.

The questions give you plenty of practice at specific National Curriculum levels so you can measure your progress against national standards.

Exercise N3

L6 **M** **1** What is seven cubed?

M **2** What is the square of two hundred?

▷ **M** shows a mental test question.

▷ ▦ means you can use a calculator.

The **Revision** pages are numbered **R1** to **R6**. These pages are full of past paper test questions at each of the relevant levels so you experience the style of question you will see in the actual tests. Each question refers you back to the relevant spread so you can go back over any content you need to practice further.

At the end to the book, there are two **Practice Test Papers** which mirror the style and content of the real thing. If you take these tests under exam conditions you will get a good idea of how you are performing. Do remember that the actual tests are slightly faster as you can write on them.

All the **Answers** are at the back of the book so you can test yourself.

Contents

Contents

How to revise using this book

A good way to revise is to start with the Revision pages (**R1** to **R6**) to see what you know and what you need to practice.

Do each one in turn.

Each question refers you back to the content that you need to practice.

To revise a topic:
▶ Read the page through slowly and carefully.
▶ Make sure you understand each step of the worked examples.
▶ Make sure you understand the information in each key point.
▶ Work through the topic questions, as they will help you identify which sorts of questions may cause problems.
▶ Read through the topic again a few days later to help you remember.

Once you are confident you understand the key ideas, set aside an hour and test yourself using Practice Test Paper 1. You can see the equipment you'll need at the start of the test – make sure you have it all ready before you start.

Remember that in the actual test you'll be able to fill in the answers on the sheet so it will take less time. You could allow yourself an extra 15 minutes in the Practice Test Papers for all the copying and filling in you need to do.

Talk to your teacher about any difficulties you have found, then move on to Practice Test Paper 2.

A place value table shows the value of each digit in a number.

$\times 10 \quad \times 10 \quad \times 10 \quad \times 10 \quad \times 10 \quad \times 10$

1000 Thousands	100 Hundreds	10 Tens	1 Units	0.1 Tenths	0.01 Hundredths	0.001 Thousandths
		4	3 •	2	5	
	4	3	2 •	5		

▶ When you multiply or divide by an integer power of 10 the digits stay in the same order.

$43.25 \times 10 = 432.5$

Write down the answer to:

a 34.7×100 **b** $65.03 \div 10$ **c** 45.6×0.001 **d** $25 \div 0.01$

....

a The digits move two places to the left: 3470
b The digits move one place to the right: 6.503
c $0.001 = \frac{1}{1000}$
45.6×0.001 is the same as $45.6 \div 1000$.
The digits move three places to the right: 0.0456
d $0.01 = \frac{1}{100}$
$25 \div 0.01$ is the same as $25 \times 100 = 2500$

> Dividing by $\frac{1}{n}$ is the same as multiplying by n.

You can round numbers to a given decimal place or significant figure.

If the next digit is 5 or more you round up: 187 is 190 to the nearest 10.

▶ To round to 2 decimal places (dp) you leave 2 digits after the decimal point: 3.8946 is 3.89 to 2 dp.
▶ To round to 1 significant figure (sf) you find the first non-zero digit and then round: $5362 = 5000$ and 0.04625 is 0.05 to 1 sf.

> A zero trapped between digits or at the end can count as a non-zero digit: 30 652 is 30 700 to 3 sf.

▶ The upper and lower bounds of a number are half the rounded amount added to and subtracted from the number.

Find the upper and lower bounds of:

a 260, which has been rounded to the nearest 10
b 3.2, which has been rounded to the nearest 0.1.

....

a Half of 10 is 5.
The upper bound is $260 + 5 = 265$.
The lower bound is $260 - 5 = 255$.
b Half of 0.1 is 0.05.
The upper bound is $3.2 + 0.05 = 3.25$.
The lower bound $3.2 - 0.05 = 3.15$.

> Imagine the number line:
>
> 3.1 ↑ 3.2 ↑ 3.3
>   3.15   3.25

Exercise N1

L5 **M** **1** Round these distances to the nearest 10 m.

    a 632 m   **b** 215 m   **c** 198 m

2 Which of the following distances are the same to one significant figure?

    248 km   302 km   251 km

3 A tower block is 200 m high to the nearest 100 m and 170 m high
to the nearest 10 m.
Write down one possible height for this tower block.

L6 **4** Copy and complete: $29 \div 10 = 29 \times 0.1$

                              $29 \div 1000 = 29 \times$ _____

5 There were 78 400 people at a football match.
Nearly 30% were children.

    a The percentage was rounded to the nearest whole number.
       What is the smallest value that the percentage could have been,
       to one decimal place?
    b What is the smallest number of children that there might have been
       at the football match? (Use your answer to part **a** to help you.)

L7 **6** Use these number cards to answer the following questions.

    | 0.2 | | 0.01 | | 2.5 | | 0.5 | | 0.004 | | 10 |

    Copy and complete:

    a $0.2 \times$ _____ $= 2$ **b** $2.5 \div$ _____ $= 250$ **c** $0.2 \times$ _____ $= 0.002$

    d Choose two cards that give the lowest possible answer.

       i _____ $\times$ _____ $=$ _____   **ii** _____ $\div$ _____ $=$ _____

    e Choose two cards that give the highest possible total.
       _____ $+$ _____ $=$ _____

    f Choose three different cards that multiply together to give
       the answer 1.

7 In a long jump competition a distance jumped was recorded as
4.32 m to the nearest centimetre.
Could the distance jumped have been longer than 4.32 m?
Explain your answer.

M **8** At a school sports day the 100 m sprint was won in a time of
18.4 seconds, measured to the nearest tenth of a second.
Between what two values does this time actually lie?

9 162 students sat an exam. Just over 48% of the students passed the exam.
The percentage was rounded to the nearest whole number.
    a What is the largest value that the percentage could have been, to 1 decimal place?
    b What is the largest number of students that passed the exam?
       (Use your answer to part **a** to help you.)

A negative number is a number less than zero.

▶ The larger the size of a negative number the further away it is from zero: ⁻5 is smaller than ⁻2.

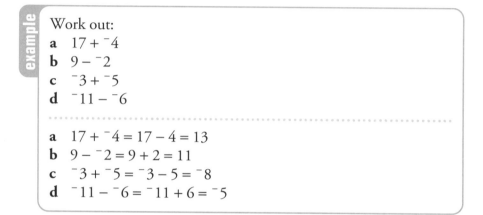

getting smaller   getting bigger

⁻10 ⁻9 ⁻8 ⁻7 ⁻6 ⁻5 ⁻4 ⁻3 ⁻2 ⁻1 0 1 2 3 4 5 6 7 8 9 10

▶ Adding a negative number is like subtracting a positive number.
Subtracting a negative number is like adding a positive number.

example

Work out:
a $17 + ^-4$
b $9 - ^-2$
c $^-3 + ^-5$
d $^-11 - ^-6$

....

a $17 + ^-4 = 17 - 4 = 13$
b $9 - ^-2 = 9 + 2 = 11$
c $^-3 + ^-5 = ^-3 - 5 = ^-8$
d $^-11 - ^-6 = ^-11 + 6 = ^-5$

▶ A factor of a number will divide exactly into that number:
the factors of 12 are 1, 2, 3, 4, 6 and 12.

▶ A prime number has two different factors, the number 1 and the number itself.

You can write a number as a product of its prime factors.

A prime factor is a factor that is also a prime number.

example

Write in prime factor form:
a 110
b 126

....

a $110 = 2 \times 55$
$\quad = 2 \times 5 \times 11$
b $126 = 2 \times 63$
$\quad = 2 \times 3 \times 21$
$\quad = 2 \times 3 \times 3 \times 7$

You can use a factor tree:

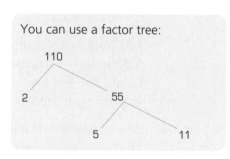

▶ You find a multiple of a number by multiplying by a whole number.
The first five multiples of 4 are: 4, 8, 12, 16, 20.

Triangle numbers can be arranged as triangles:

They form the sequence: 1,   3,   6,   10,   ...

The differences between triangle numbers increase by one each time.

Exercise N2

L5 **M** **1** I am thinking of a two-digit number that is a multiple of seven.
The digits add up to six.
What number am I thinking of?

M **2 a** Subtract seven from minus two.
b Add nine to minus four.

M **3** Write down the first multiple of nine over one hundred.

4 I am thinking of a two-digit number that is a multiple of 5.
The difference between the digits is 3.
What possible numbers am I thinking of?

5 Here is a list of numbers

$^-6$ $^-3$ $^-2$ 1   4   5   7

   a What is the total of all seven numbers in the list?
   b Choose three numbers from the list to give the lowest possible total.
   Write down the three numbers and their total.
   You may not use any number more than once.
   c Write down the numbers from the list that give a total of 3.

L6 **6** A solid cuboid is made from 36 one-centimetre cube blocks.
It is 3 cm high.
Write down possible dimensions of the other sides.

7 Choose from these number cards to answer the questions.

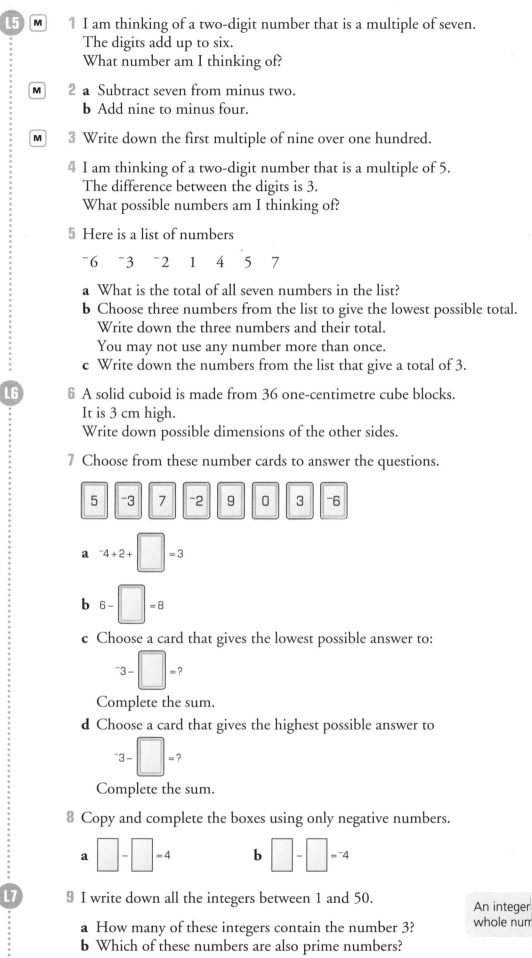

   a $^-4 + 2 + \boxed{} = 3$

   b $6 - \boxed{} = 8$

   c Choose a card that gives the lowest possible answer to:

   $^-3 - \boxed{} = ?$

   Complete the sum.
   d Choose a card that gives the highest possible answer to

   $^-3 - \boxed{} = ?$

   Complete the sum.

8 Copy and complete the boxes using only negative numbers.

   a $\boxed{} - \boxed{} = 4$ **b** $\boxed{} - \boxed{} = {}^-4$

L7 **9** I write down all the integers between 1 and 50.

   a How many of these integers contain the number 3?
   b Which of these numbers are also prime numbers?

An integer is a positive or negative whole number.

10 Write the number 48 as a product of prime factors.

11 Write 60 as a product of prime factors.

5

Square numbers can be arranged as squares:

. 1   .. 4   ... 9   16   25

KEYWORDS

Power	Cube number
Index	Square root
Square number	Cube root

A square number is the result of multiplying a number by itself:

$1 \times 1 = 1, \quad 2 \times 2 = 4, \quad 3 \times 3 = 9, \quad 4 \times 4 = 16, \quad 5 \times 5 = 25, \ldots$

You can write square numbers using an index or power:

$$1^2 \qquad 2^2 \qquad 3^2 \qquad 4^2 \qquad 5^2$$

Cube numbers use the power 3:

$1^3 = 1 \times 1 \times 1 = 1,$
$2^3 = 2 \times 2 \times 2 = 8,$
$3^3 = 3 \times 3 \times 3 = 27,$
$4^3 = 4 \times 4 \times 4 = 64, \ldots$

▶ A power shows the number of times a number is multiplied by itself.
4^5 means $4 \times 4 \times 4 \times 4 \times 4$
(You say '4 to the power 5'.)

A root of a number is the reverse of a power.

▶ The square root $\sqrt{}$ of a number is the opposite of squaring.
$\sqrt{64} = 8 \quad (8 \times 8 = 64)$

▶ The cube root $\sqrt[3]{}$ of a number is the opposite of cubing.
$\sqrt[3]{64} = 4 \quad (4 \times 4 \times 4 = 64)$

You can multiply and divide powers of the same numbers.
Use these rules:

▶ When you multiply, add the powers.
▶ When you divide, subtract the powers.

Cube numbers can be arranged as cubes:

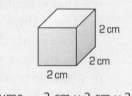

Volume $= 2\,cm \times 2\,cm \times 2\,cm$
$= 8\,cm^3$

To use these rules the main number has to be the same.

> **example**
>
> Simplify:
>
> **a** $4^3 \times 4^5$ **b** $7^9 \div 7^4$
>
> ....
>
> **a** $4^3 \times 4^5 = 4^{3+5} = 4^8$ **b** $7^9 \div 7^4 = 7^{9-4} = 7^5$

▶ When you calculate the power of a number it will get much bigger or much smaller quite quickly.

The powers of 3 are: 3, 9, 27, 81, 243, 729, 2187, …
The powers of 0.2 are: 0.2, 0.04, 0.008, 0.0016, 0.00032, 0.000064, …

Exercise N3

L6 **M** **1** What is seven cubed? 343

M **2** What is the square of two hundred? 40000

M **3** What is the square root of forty-nine? 7

M **4** What is the square root of ten thousand? 100,000

M **5** What is the cube root of one hundred and twenty-five? 5

6 Choose from these numbers:

$$1^7 \qquad 2^5 \qquad 3^4 \qquad 4^3 \qquad 9^2$$

a Which is the largest number? 9^2
b Which number is not a square number? 3^4
c Which numbers are equal?

7 Which of the following is not a square number?

$$3^4 \qquad 5^3 \qquad 7^2 \qquad 9^3$$

8 Which of the following is not a cube number?

$$2^6 \qquad 3^5 \qquad 6^3 \qquad 8^2$$

L7 **9** Seven to the power four multiplied by seven to the power five is equal to seven to the power what?

M **10** Three to the power eight divided by three to the power two is equal to three to the power what?

M **11** What would be the last digit in:
a twenty-two to the power three
b ninety-five to the power seven
c four hundred and fifty-six to the power four?

12 Write down the value of k if $81 = 3^k$.

13 $4^9 = 262\ 144$
Work out 4^8.

M **14** Eight to the power twelve divided by eight to the power of eleven is equal to what?

15 $2^7 = 128$
Work out 2^8.

16 $10^5 = 100\ 000$
Work out 10^{10}.

17 Write down the values of x and y when:
$256 = 16^x = 4^y$

In a fraction $\dfrac{3}{5}$ ← the top number is the numerator
← the bottom number is the denominator

▶ To compare and order fractions and decimals you can:
  ▷ change them all into decimals, or
  ▷ change them all into fractions with the same denominator.

▶ You change a fraction to a decimal by dividing:
$\frac{3}{8} = 3 \div 8 = 0.375$

▶ You change a decimal to a fraction using place value:
  ▷ 0.4 has 1 decimal place $0.4 = \frac{4}{10}$ (1 zero)
  ▷ 0.23 has 2 decimal places $0.23 = \frac{23}{100}$ (2 zeros)
  ▷ 0.06 has 2 decimal places $0.06 = \frac{6}{100}$ (2 zeros)

You use this method with terminating decimals.

Some fractions have decimal equivalents that recur:

$\frac{1}{3} = 0.\dot{3}$ $\frac{2}{3} = 0.\dot{6}$

The dot shows that the digit below it recurs.
$\frac{1}{3} = 0.\dot{3} = 0.333 \ldots$

▶ To add or subtract fractions they must have the same denominator.

example

a $\frac{2}{5} + \frac{3}{8}$ **b** $\frac{5}{6} - \frac{1}{4}$

a $\frac{2}{5} + \frac{3}{8} = \frac{16}{40} + \frac{15}{40} = \frac{31}{40}$ **b** $\frac{5}{6} - \frac{1}{4} = \frac{10}{12} - \frac{3}{12} = \frac{7}{12}$

▶ To multiply fractions you multiply the numerators and denominators.

example

a $\frac{3}{7} \times \frac{4}{5}$ **b** $\frac{5}{8} \times \frac{2}{9}$

a $\frac{3}{7} \times \frac{4}{5} = \frac{3 \times 4}{7 \times 5} = \frac{12}{35}$ **b** $\frac{5}{8} \times \frac{2}{9} = \frac{5 \times 2}{8 \times 9} = \frac{10}{72} = \frac{5}{36}$

▶ To divide fractions you turn the second fraction upside-down and change ÷ to ×.

$\frac{3}{5} \div \frac{7}{8} = \frac{3}{5} \times \frac{8}{7}$
$= \frac{3 \times 8}{5 \times 7}$
$= \frac{24}{35}$

To multiply or divide with a mixed number change it to an improper fraction first: $3\frac{1}{2} \times 1\frac{1}{3} = \frac{7}{2} \times \frac{4}{3}$

A percentage is a fraction out of 100: 12% means $\frac{12}{100}$.

▶ To change a decimal to a percentage you multiply by 100.

$0.375 = 37.5\%$ $(0.375 \times 100 = 37.5)$

Fractions, decimals and percentages are three ways of writing the same number.

Exercise N4

L5

1 Copy and complete:

    a $\frac{1}{2}$ of 50 = $\frac{1}{4}$ of _100_

    b $\frac{1}{3}$ of 120 = $\frac{2}{5}$ of _800_

    c $\frac{3}{4}$ of 40 = $\frac{1}{3}$ of _90_

M 2 Each diagram below is drawn on a square grid.
Write what percentage of each diagram is blue.

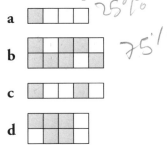

    a _25%_

    b _75%_

    c

    d

3 What fraction of each diagram is blue?
Write your fraction as simply as possible.

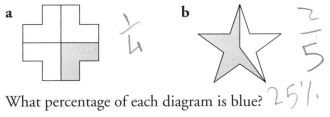

    a $\frac{1}{4}$ **b** $\frac{2}{5}$

    What percentage of each diagram is blue? _25%_

L6 **M** 4 What is one-quarter of two-fifths of fifty?

5 Work out:

    a $\frac{3}{8} + \frac{5}{16}$ **b** $\frac{8}{9} - \frac{8}{27}$

6 Which is bigger: 58% or $\frac{5}{8}$? Show your working.

7 Which is smaller: 38% or $\frac{3}{8}$? Show your working.

8 **a** How many fifths are there in $2\frac{1}{10}$?

    b Work out $2\frac{1}{10} \div \frac{3}{10}$

L7 9 Choose from this list:

    $\frac{1}{2}$ $\frac{3}{8}$ $\frac{2}{5}$ $\frac{4}{7}$ $\frac{1}{10}$

    a Which two fractions have the lowest product?

    _____ × _____ = _____

    b Find three fractions that add up to 1.

    c Which fraction has a recurring decimal equivalent?

10 Choose from this list:

    0.2   0.25   0.4   0.8   2   5

    a Which two numbers give the lowest possible product?

    _____ × _____ = _____

    b Which two numbers give the answer 10?

    _____ ÷ _____ = 10

▶ You can use a multiplier to increase or decrease by a percentage.

KEYWORDS

Percentage	Proportion
Ratio	Unitary method

example

a Increase £56 by 15%.
b Decrease £68 by 6%.

....

a $100\% + 15\% = 115\%$ $\quad$ $115\% = 1.15$ $\quad$ $1.15 \times 56 = £64.40$
b $100\% - 6\% = 94\%$ $\quad$ $94\% = 0.94$ $\quad$ $0.94 \times 68 = £63.92$

Check:
15% is $\frac{15}{100} \times £56 = £8.40$
£56 + £8.40 = £64.40

▶ Ratio compares the size of one part with the size of another part.
If you mix 2 parts juice with 5 parts water the ratio is 2 : 5.

You can use ratio when things are in proportion.

example

These triangles are similar. Find x.

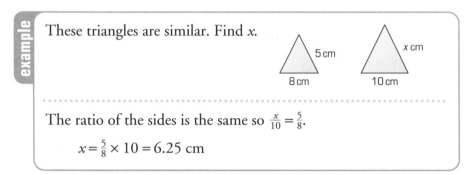

The ratio of the sides is the same so $\frac{x}{10} = \frac{5}{8}$.

$x = \frac{5}{8} \times 10 = 6.25$ cm

5 : 8 or $\frac{5}{8}$ is the ratio of the shorter side to the longer side.

You can share an amount in a given ratio.
▶ To share an amount in the ratio 3 : 5:
  ▷ Find the total number of shares: $3 + 5 = 8$
  ▷ Divide the amount by 8.
  ▷ Multiply by 3 for the first share and by 5 for the second share.

example

a Share £98 in the ratio 4 : 3.
b Share £48 in the ratio 1 : 2 : 3.

....

a $4 + 3 = 7$ $\qquad$ $98 \div 7 = 14$
$\quad 4 \times 14 = 56$
$\quad 3 \times 14 = 42$
$\quad 4 : 3 = £56 : £42$
b $1 + 2 + 3 = 6$ $\qquad$ $48 \div 6 = 8$
$\quad 2 \times 8 = 16$
$\quad 3 \times 8 = 24$
$\quad 1 : 2 : 3 = £8 : £16 : £24$

Check:
£56 + £42 = £98

Check:
£8 + £16 + £24 = £48

▶ A proportion compares the size of a part with the whole.

You can use the unitary method to solve problems involving proportions.

example

A 160 g cereal bar has 220 calories. Find the number of calories in 100 g.

....

160 g: 220 calories
1 g: 1.375 calories (220 ÷ 160)
100 g: 137.5 calories

You find out the number of calories in 1 g.

Exercise N5

L5

1 25% of a number is 11. What is that number?

2 Calculate **a** 15% of £32 **b** 17.5% of £46.

3 I am thinking of a number. 10% of the number is 76.
Work out 30% of the number.

4 5% of a number is 24.
Find $12\frac{1}{2}$% of the number.

5 Gareth mixes 1 carton of grapefruit juice with 3 cartons
of orange juice in a jug.
What is the ratio of grapefruit juice to orange juice in the jug?

6 In a toy train set the ratio of engines to carriages is always
the same.
In the starter set there are 2 engines and 12 carriages.
In the super set there are 5 engines. How many carriages are there
in the super set?

L6

7 Share **a** £50 in the ratio 2 : 3 **b** £144 in the ratio 5 : 4.

8 In a 400 g tin of salmon there are 250 calories.
How many calories would there be in a 150 g serving?

9 Joshua is 12 years old. Reuben is 9 years old.
The ratio of their ages is 12 : 9, written as simply as possible the ratio is 4 : 3.
a When Joshua is 18 years old, what will the ratio of Joshua's age to Reuben's age be?
Write this ratio as simply as possible.
b When Reuben is 18 years old, what will the ratio of Joshua's age to Reuben's age be?
c Find Joshua's and Reuben's ages when the ratio was 2 : 1.

L7

10 The table shows the numbers of different ice-creams sold and the amount of money taken at a
theatre show one evening.

Ice-cream	Choc-ice	Cornet	Tub	Total
Number sold	40	130	80	250
Amount taken	£60	£130	£100	£290

a What percentage of the ice-creams sold were cornets?
b What percentage of the total takings were for cornets?
c What type of ice-cream is more expensive, choc-ice or tub?
Explain how you found your answer.

11 Copy and complete the following:

a To increase an amount by 37% multiply by _____
b To decrease an amount by 16% multiply by _____

12 **a** Increase £28 by 12%. **b** Decrease £28 by 15%.

13 A girls' school has a mixed sixth form. The ratio of boys to girls in the school is 1 : 24.
There are 1550 pupils at the school. How many of the pupils are boys?

14 The price of a pair of shoes was reduced by 10% for each day of a sale.
On the Monday of the sale the price of a pair of shoes was £36.
a How much would you have to pay if you bought the shoes on the Thursday?
b How many days would it take before the shoes cost less than £20?
c Explain why the price of the shoes would never be reduced to nothing.

You need to use the correct order of operations to work out a sum.

example

Calculate:

$$\frac{(4.2 - 1.7)^2}{10} + \frac{19.1 \times 3}{\sqrt{12 \times 3}}$$

First work out the **brackets**:
$$= \frac{2.5^2}{10} + \frac{19.1 \times 3}{\sqrt{36}}$$

Next work out **index** or **root**:
$$= \frac{6.25}{10} + \frac{19.1 \times 3}{6}$$

Then do **multiplication** and **division**:
$$= \frac{6.25}{10} + \frac{57.3}{6}$$

$$= 0.625 + 9.55$$

Finally do **addition** and **subtraction**: $= 10.175$

The square root contains a hidden bracket: $(12 \times 3) = 36$.

▶ The operations are paired together as **inverse** operations:
  ▷ Index and root $6^2 = 36$ $\sqrt{36} = 6$
  ▷ Multiplication and division $6 \times 7 = 42$ $42 \div 7 = 6$
  ▷ Addition and subtraction $5 + 3 = 8$ $8 - 3 = 5$

Inverse operations have the opposite effect; they undo each other.

You can check that your answer is correct by estimating.

▶ You estimate answers by rounding to 1 or 2 sf.

Look back at N1 for help with rounding.

example

Estimate $\dfrac{3.7 \times 53.2}{18.94}$.

Round to 1 sf:

$$\frac{4 \times 50}{20} = \frac{200}{20} = 10$$

▶ When you multiply by a number between 0 and 1 the answer is smaller.
▶ When you divide by a number between 0 and 1 the answer is bigger.

If you know the size of the answer you expect to get you can spot errors.

example

Look at these number cards.

0.1	0.01	0.5	10	5	1

a Choose two of the cards to give the lowest possible answer: ▢ × ▢ = ▢

b Choose two of the cards to make an answer of 20: ▢ ÷ ▢ = 20

a Multiply the two smallest numbers to give the smallest answer: 0.1 × 0.01 = 0.001

b There are 20 halves in 10: 10 ÷ 0.5 = 20

Exercise N6

L5

1 James wrote $\dfrac{16 \times 35}{3} = 188$.

Without doing the calculation, explain how you know the answer is incorrect.

2 Jenny wrote $\dfrac{10.5 + 7.5}{1.5} = 7 + 5$

Explain why the sum Jenny wrote is correct.

3 Eddie wrote $\dfrac{60 - 12}{6 - 2} = 10 - 6$

  a Without doing any working, explain why the sum Eddie wrote is incorrect.
  b Work out the correct answer.

L6

4 Work out $12 + \dfrac{14.7}{0.3}$.

5 Work out $57 - \sqrt{(9 \times 8 \times 18)}$.

6 Work out $\dfrac{35}{\sqrt{3^2 + 4^2}}$

7 Work out $\dfrac{\sqrt{12}}{\sqrt{3}}$

8 Work out $\sqrt{50^2 - 48^2}$

9 Explain why the answer to $1 \div \left(\dfrac{1}{4} + \dfrac{1}{3} \right)$ must be greater than 1. Work out the answer.

L7

10 Estimate the answer to:

  a $\dfrac{27.8 \times 11.2}{15.1}$ **b** $\dfrac{53.1 + 19}{12.2 - 4.9}$

11 Work out $\dfrac{15.3}{\sqrt{9}} + \dfrac{2^3}{5 - 1}$.

12 Calculate $\dfrac{2}{5} + \dfrac{\sqrt{(4^3 + 6^2)}}{7.2 - 4.7}$.

M **13** Choose your answers from this list:

    3   4   5   6   7

  a Which is the best estimate for 8.3×0.47?
  b Which is the best estimate for $73.2 \div 12.4$?

14 Choose your answers from this list

    0.00003   0.0003   0.003   0.03   0.3   3   30

  a Which is the best estimate for 52.4×0.006?
  b Which is the best estimate for $52.4 \div 1.7$?

15 Work out $\dfrac{4^2 + 7.5^2}{\sqrt{4^2 + 7.5^2}}$

16 Work out $2.6 + \sqrt{\dfrac{8^2 - (5 \times 3.2)}{18 \div 1.5}}$

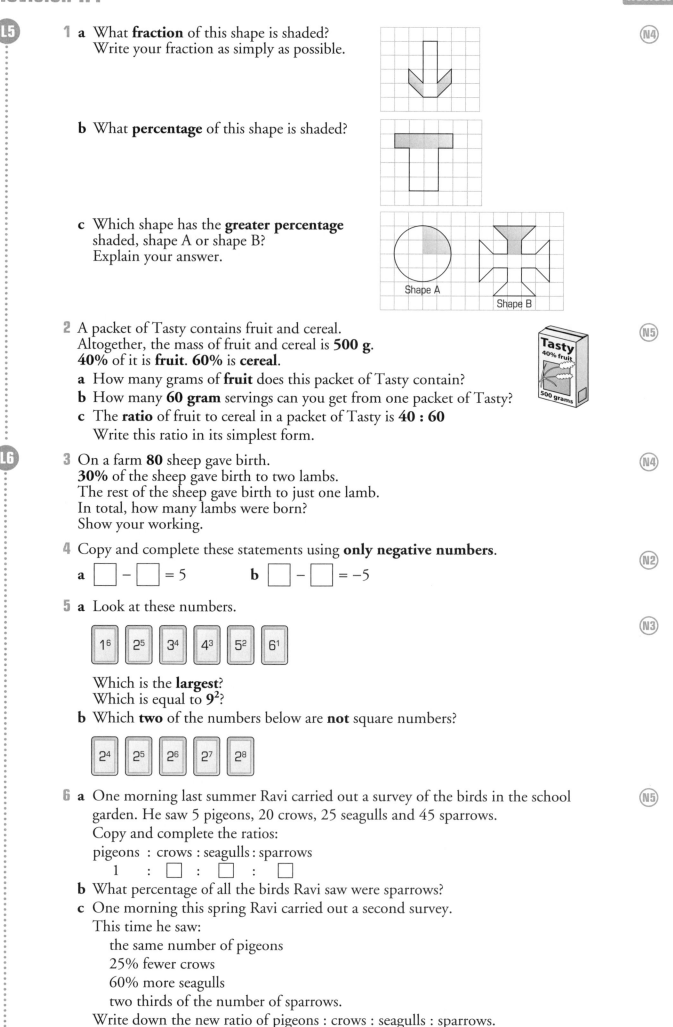

L5

1 a What **fraction** of this shape is shaded?
Write your fraction as simply as possible.

b What **percentage** of this shape is shaded?

c Which shape has the **greater percentage** shaded, shape A or shape B?
Explain your answer.

Shape A

Shape B

N4

2 A packet of Tasty contains fruit and cereal.
Altogether, the mass of fruit and cereal is **500 g**.
40% of it is **fruit**. **60%** is **cereal**.
a How many grams of **fruit** does this packet of Tasty contain?
b How many **60 gram** servings can you get from one packet of Tasty?
c The **ratio** of fruit to cereal in a packet of Tasty is **40 : 60**
Write this ratio in its simplest form.

N5

L6

3 On a farm **80** sheep gave birth.
30% of the sheep gave birth to two lambs.
The rest of the sheep gave birth to just one lamb.
In total, how many lambs were born?
Show your working.

N4

4 Copy and complete these statements using **only negative numbers**.
a ☐ – ☐ = 5 **b** ☐ – ☐ = –5

N2

5 a Look at these numbers.

1^6 2^5 3^4 4^3 5^2 6^1

Which is the **largest**?
Which is equal to 9^2?
b Which **two** of the numbers below are **not** square numbers?

2^4 2^5 2^6 2^7 2^8

N3

6 a One morning last summer Ravi carried out a survey of the birds in the school garden. He saw 5 pigeons, 20 crows, 25 seagulls and 45 sparrows.
Copy and complete the ratios:
pigeons : crows : seagulls : sparrows
    1   : ☐ : ☐ : ☐
b What percentage of all the birds Ravi saw were sparrows?
c One morning this spring Ravi carried out a second survey.
This time he saw:
    the same number of pigeons
    25% fewer crows
    60% more seagulls
    two thirds of the number of sparrows.
Write down the new ratio of pigeons : crows : seagulls : sparrows.

N5

L7

7 At an athletics meeting, the discus throws are measured to the nearest centimetre.

  a Viv's best throw was measured as 35.42 m.

    Could Viv's throw actually have been more than 35.42 m?

    Explain your answer.

  b Chris won the hurdles race in a time of 14.6 seconds measured to the nearest tenth of a second.

    Between what two values does Chris's time actually lie?

N1

8 David is studying blood cells through a microscope.

The diameter of a red cell is 0.000714 cm and the diameter of a white cell is 0.001243 cm.

  a Use a calculator to work out the difference between the diameter of a red cell and the diameter of a white cell.

    Give your answer in **millimetres**.

David wants to explain how small the cells are.

He calculates how many white cells would fit across a full stop which has a diameter of 0.65 mm.

  b How many whole white cells would fit across the full stop?

N4

9 a From the six numbers listed, write down the **best** estimate of the answer to:

    $72.34 \div 8.91$

    6   7   8   9   10   11

  b From the six numbers listed, write down the **best** estimate of the answer to:

    $32.7 \div 0.48$

    1.2   1.6   12   16   120   160

  c Estimate the answer to $\dfrac{8.62 + 22.1}{5.23}$.

    Give your answer to **1 significant figure**.

  d Estimate the answer to $\dfrac{28.6 + 24.4}{5.67 \times 4.02}$.

N6

10 a Write the values of k and m.

    $64 = 8^2 = 4k = 2^m$

  b $2^{15} = 32\,768$

    Find the value of 2^{14}.

N3

You need to be able to calculate in your head.
You can use place value for some calculations.

KEYWORDS
Partitioning   Compensating

example

Given that $430 \times 5.8 = 2494$, find:
a $43\,000 \times 58$ b 0.43×58 c $24\,940 \div 43$

a $43\,000$ is 100 times bigger, 58 is 10 times bigger, so answer is 1000 times bigger: $43\,000 \times 58 = 2\,494\,000$
b 0.43 is 1000 times smaller, 58 is 10 times bigger so answer is 100 times smaller: $0.43 \times 58 = 24.94$
c $24\,940 = 10 \times 2494$, $43 = 430 \div 10$, so answer is 100 times bigger: $24\,940 \div 43 = 580$

Always use rounding to check your answer is the right size.

Use fractions:
$$\frac{2494 \times 10}{430 \div 10} = \frac{2494 \times 10}{430 \times \frac{1}{10}}$$
$$= \frac{2494 \times 10 \times 10}{430}$$

Doubling and halving are useful strategies.

example

Find   a 17.5% of 92   b 22% of 86

a 10% of $92 = 9.2$, so 5% is $\frac{1}{2}$ of $9.2 = 4.6$ and 2.5% is 2.3 ($\frac{1}{2}$ of 4.6).
17.5% is $10\% + 5\% + 2.5\%$, so the answer is $9.2 + 4.6 + 2.3 = 16.1$.
b 10% of $86 = 8.6$, 1% is 0.86, so 11% is $8.6 + 0.86 = 9.46$. 22% is double 11%, so the answer is $2 \times 9.46 = 18.92$.

You can partition a number into place value parts, or round then compensate.

example

a Find the time difference between 9.47 am and 1.14 pm.
b Calculate $12.71 - 8.86$.
c Calculate 49×372.

a Split up the time line.

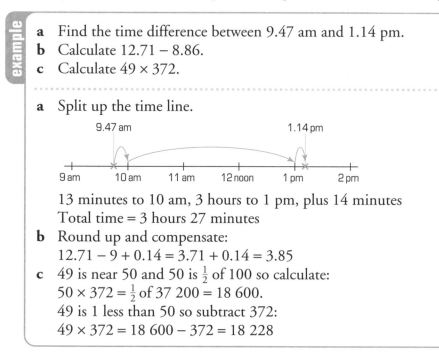

13 minutes to 10 am, 3 hours to 1 pm, plus 14 minutes
Total time = 3 hours 27 minutes
b Round up and compensate:
$12.71 - 9 + 0.14 = 3.71 + 0.14 = 3.85$
c 49 is near 50 and 50 is $\frac{1}{2}$ of 100 so calculate:
$50 \times 372 = \frac{1}{2}$ of $37\,200 = 18\,600$.
49 is 1 less than 50 so subtract 372:
$49 \times 372 = 18\,600 - 372 = 18\,228$

Imagine the number line in part **b**:

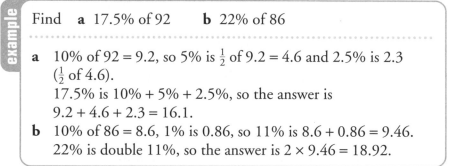

You can simplify fractions by cancelling common factors.

example

Find   a $\frac{4}{27} \times \frac{6}{11}$ b 17% of $80\,000$

a $\frac{4}{\cancel{27}_{9}} \times \frac{\cancel{6}^{2}}{11} = \frac{4}{9} \times \frac{2}{11} = \frac{8}{99}$ b $\frac{17}{100} \times 80\,000 = 17 \times 800 = 13\,600$

You can change between fractions, decimals and percentages to make it easier to calculate.

L5

1 This is how Hazel calculates 15% of 720 in her head:

> 10% of 720 is 72
> 5% of 720 is 36
>
> So 15% is 72 + 36 = 108

> In this exercise remember to write down enough working to show that you haven't used a calculator.

Show how Hazel can work out
a 17.5% of 140   **b** 35% of 220

2 The entrance charge to an exhibition is £12.
   a 31 people visited the exhibition one day.
      How much money did they pay altogether?
   b On another day the exhibition took £600 in entrance charges.
      How many people visited the exhibition on that day?

3 Work out 29×37.

4 Forty-two tins are packed into a box. Each tin weighs 375 g.
   Work out the total weight of the tins in the box.

L6

5 A town gets an average of 42.5 cm of rain per year.
   How much rain could this town expect to get over 20 years?

6 Mark's hand span is 9.8 cm.
   Jenny's hand span is 10% less. What is Jenny's hand span?

7 Given that $42.3 \times 7.4 = 313.02$, work out:
   a 423×74 **b** 0.423×7.4 **c** 4.23×740 **d** $31\,302 \div 42.3$

8 Show how you can increase 485 by 19%.
   Write down your answer.

9 On a farm 60 cows gave birth. 20% of the cows gave birth to two calves.
   The rest of the cows gave birth to one calf each.
   In total, how many calves were born?

10 Use each number from the following list once to make the calculations below.

   2   3   4   5   7   8

   The first one has been done for you.
   a $265 = 543 - 278$ **b** $911 = \_\_\_ + \_\_\_$ **c** $287 = \_\_\_ - \_\_\_$

11 A unit fraction has numerator 1 and denominator greater than 1.
   $\dfrac{1}{4}, \dfrac{1}{7}, \dfrac{1}{10}$ are all examples of unit fractions.

   You can write a fraction as the sum of unit fractions, for example $\dfrac{3}{4} = \dfrac{1}{2} + \dfrac{1}{4}$.

   a For what fraction can you write the sum $\dfrac{1}{6} + \dfrac{1}{5}$?

   b Write $\dfrac{7}{12}$ as the sum of two unit fractions if one of the fractions is $\dfrac{1}{3}$.

   c Write $\dfrac{16}{63}$ as the sum of two unit fractions.

L7

12 Mrs Brown borrows £800.
   There are two ways in which she can borrow the money:
   i   at an interest rate of 5% for five years
   ii at an interest rate of 8% for 3 years.
   Which option involves paying less interest and by how much?

▶ To add or subtract decimals:
  ▷ write the sum down the page
  ▷ line up the units so that the decimal points are underneath each other.

example

a $9.0032 + 0.765$ **b** $64 - 0.98$ **c** $203.87 + 7.2009$

a $\begin{array}{r} 9.0032 \\ + 0.765 \\ \hline 9.7682 \end{array}$ **b** $\begin{array}{r} 64 \\ - 0.98 \\ \hline 63.02 \end{array}$ **c** $\begin{array}{r} 203.87 \\ + 7.2009 \\ \hline 211.0709 \end{array}$

Estimate answers by rounding before calculating.

If there is no decimal point shown it will be after the units digit.

To multiply with decimals you can use an equivalent calculation.

▶ The answer will have the same number of places after the decimal point as there are in total in the question.

example

a 4.2×0.006 **b** 0.008×0.03 **c** 0.056×0.5

a $42 \times 6 = 252$
There are 4 dps.
4.2×0.006
$= 0.0252$

b $8 \times 3 = 24$
There are 5 dps.
0.008×0.03
$= 0.00024$

c $56 \times 5 = 280$
There are 4 dps.
0.056×0.5
$= 0.0280$

A zero at the end of a number will count as one of the places.

For larger numbers you may need to do long multiplication.

example

Work out 12.3×0.46.

Calculate 123×46:
$\begin{array}{r} 123 \\ \times\ 46 \\ \hline 738 \\ 4920 \\ \hline 5658 \end{array}$ $\begin{array}{l} (123 \times 6) \\ (123 \times 40) \end{array}$

There are 3 decimal places, so $12.3 \times 0.46 = 5.658$.

Remember to estimate:
12.3×0.46
$\approx 12 \times 0.5$
$= 6$.

▶ To divide with decimals, multiply both numbers by the same power of 10 to make the divisor an integer.

The divisor is the number you divide by.

example

a $0.975 \div 0.03$ **b** $672 \div 1.6$

a Multiply by 100: $97.5 \div 3$

$\begin{array}{r} 3)97.5 \\ -\ 90.0 \\ \hline 7.5 \\ -\ 6.0 \\ \hline 1.5 \\ 1.5 \\ \hline 0.0 \end{array}$ $\begin{array}{l} (3 \times 30) \\ \\ (3 \times 2) \\ \\ (3 \times 0.5) \end{array}$

$0.975 \div 0.03 = 32.5$

b Multiply by 10: $6720 \div 16$

$\begin{array}{r} 16)6720 \\ -\ 6400 \\ \hline 320 \\ -\ 320 \\ \hline 0 \end{array}$ $\begin{array}{l} (16 \times 400) \\ \\ (16 \times 20) \end{array}$

$672 \div 1.6 = 420$

Exercise N8

L5 [M] **1** What is six point seven plus two point four?

[M] **2** If one pen costs forty-two pence, how many pens could I buy for four pounds twenty pence?

3 Joshua makes wooden toys to sell.
He sells each toy for £3.80.

    a He sells 31 toys.
How much does he get for the 31 toys?

    b Joshua has a box of 500 nails.
He uses 17 nails in each toy that he makes.
How many complete toys can he make using the box of 500 nails?

4 The entrance fee to a children's play farm is £1.50 for adults.

    a 260 adults visit the farm one Saturday.
How much money did the farm take that day?

    b The farm took £750 in entrance money one Sunday.
How many adults paid to visit the farm that Sunday?

5 A student pays £4 to travel to and from school each week.
There are 39 school weeks in a year.

    a How much does the student pay to travel to and from school in a year?

    The students could buy a season ticket that would allow travel to and
from school for all of the 39 weeks.
It would cost £117.

    b How much is that per week?

L6 [M] **6** What is nought point eight divided by nought point nought one?

[M] **7** What is nought point three two divided by nought point one?

[M] **8** Look at this calculation:

    $612 \div 18 = 34$

    What is six hundred and twelve divided by one point eight?

[M] **9** How many nought point two's are there in twelve?

10 Copy, complete and find the answer:

    a $76.32 \div 0.4 = 763.2 \div \underline{} = \underline{}$
    b $4.923 \div 0.05 = \underline{} \div 5 = \underline{}$

L7 [M] **11** Look at this calculation:

    $14 \times 56 = 784$

    What is seven hundred and eighty-four divided by one point four?

[M] **12** Look at this calculation:

    $564 \div 47 = 12$

    What is five hundred and sixty-four divided by one point two?

19

A calculator uses the standard order of operations.
You need to watch out for hidden operations.

▶ There is a hidden bracket in the denominator of a fraction.

example

Work out $\dfrac{2.78 \times 6.9}{2.5 + 15.9}$

You can use the memory for the denominator:

| 2 | . | 5 | + | 1 | 5 | . | 9 | = | M in | C |

| 2 | . | 7 | 8 | × | 6 | . | 9 | ÷ | MR | = |

or use brackets:

| 2 | . | 7 | 8 | × | 6 | . | 9 | ÷ | (| 2 | . | 5 | + | 1 | 5 | . | 9 |) | = |

The answer is 1.0425.

A square root may contain a hidden bracket:

$\sqrt{12 + 4} = \sqrt{16} = \pm 4$.

The calculator will only show the positive answer.

▶ Press × between adjacent brackets.

example

Work out $(37 - 6.25)(13.4 + 1.6)$

You press: | (| 3 | 7 | − | 6 | . | 2 | 5 |) | × | (| 1 | 3 | . | 4 | + | 1 | . | 6 |) | = |
The answer is 461.25.

These special buttons will make calculating simpler.

▶ Use x^2 and x^3 to square and cube.

▶ Use x^y to find other powers.
To find 3^4, input | 3 | x^y | 4 |.

▶ Input fractions and mixed numbers using $a^{b\!c}$.
Press the button again to convert to a decimal.

Always estimate calculations to check your answers are correct.

▶ Change the sign of a number by using the +/− button.

You must give sensible answers to problems.

example

a Work out £25.99 ÷ 7
b A shelf 2 m long is filled with files 42 cm wide.
How many files are there?

a $25.99 \div 7 = 3.712857 \ldots$
Answer: £3.71
Money answers must be rounded to a whole number of pence.
b 2 m = 200 cm
$200 \div 42 = 4.7619 \ldots$
Answer: 4 files
Round down to the nearest whole number of files.

The answer must be a whole number.

Exercise N9

L5 **1** In a trampoline competition the level of difficulty of each competitor's routine is given a rating.
The competitor's routine is given a mark out of ten by each of six judges.
Their overall score is calculated as follows:

▷ Look at all six marks. Remove the lowest and highest mark.
▷ Add up the remaining four marks and divide by four to give an average mark.
▷ Multiply the average mark by the level of difficulty rating.

a Jane has a level of difficulty rating of 4.3.
Her routine was given these marks:

7.2   5.9   6.4   7.8   6.6   6.4

i Write down the calculator sequence you would use to calculate Jane's score.
ii Calculate Jane's score.

b Jane needs to score at least 42 in the next round of the competition.
She chooses a routine with level of difficulty rating 3.9.
Explain why Jane has made a poor decision. Show your working.

L6 **2** Steve wants to find a value of x that makes x^2 equal to $5 - x$.
He constructs a table that looks like this.

x	x^2	$5 - x$	Difference
1	1	4	3
2	4	3	1

A value of x lies between 1 and 2.
Find the two numbers with one decimal place that x lies between.

3 The sides of a rectangle are given as x and $10 - x$.
The area of the rectangle is 18 to the nearest whole number.

Area of rectangle $= x(10 - x) = 18$

Use a table like this to find two numbers with one decimal place that x lies between.

x	$10 - x$	Area
1	9	9
2	8	

L7 **4** A car was driven at an average speed of 32 miles per hour.
The car used petrol at a rate of 1 litre for 13 km.

a Calculate how many litres of petrol were used in 1 hour of travel.
(5 miles ≈ 8 km)
Show your working and write down the full calculator display.
b Write your answer to a sensible degree of accuracy.

5 A baby giraffe was born that was 1.42 metres high.
Suppose it grew at a rate of $\frac{1}{2}$ an inch every hour.
About how many days old would the giraffe be when it was 4 metres high?
(Take 1 inch = 2.54 cm)

An **expression** is a collection of numbers and letters linked by operations.
Each part of an expression is called a **term**.
Like terms have the same combination of letters.

▶ You can only add or subtract like terms.

> **example**
>
> Simplify: **a** $3a + 4a + 2b - a - ab$ **b** $5a \times 3b$
>
> ....
>
> **a** Group like terms together, then add or subtract them:
> $3a + 4a + 2b - a - ab = 3a + 4a - a + 2b - ab = 6a + 2b - ab$
> **b** Multiply the numbers and letters separately:
> $5a \times 3b = 5 \times 3 \times a \times b = 15ab$

The sign in front of the term belongs to that term.

You may need to expand brackets to simplify expressions.

▶ When multiplying out brackets, multiply all the terms inside the
bracket by the term outside the bracket.

> **example**
>
> Expand:
> **a** $4(a + 3)$ **b** $3(2a - 5)$ **c** $5(a - 3) - 2(a - 4)$
>
> ....
>
> **a** $4a + 12$ **b** $6a - 15$ **c** $5a - 15 - 2a + 8 = 3a - 7$

When factorising, look for a number or letter that is common to each term.

> **example**
>
> Factorise:
> **a** $3a - 15$ **b** $6a + 8b$ **c** $2a + ab$
>
> ....
>
> **a** $3(a - 5)$ **b** $2(3a + 4b)$ **c** $a(2 + b)$

Multiplying powers of the same letter is just like multiplying powers of
the same number.

See N3 for powers of numbers.

▶ To multiply you add the powers, to divide you subtract the powers.

> **example**
>
> Simplify:
>
> **a** $a^4 \times a^3$ **b** $\dfrac{a^7}{a^2}$ **c** $4a \times 3a^2$
>
> ....
>
> **a** $a^{4+3} = a^7$ **b** $a^{7-2} = a^5$ **c** $4 \times 3 \times a^{1+2} = 12a^3$

a^3 means $a \times a \times a$.
$3a^2$ means $3 \times a \times a$.

You can add or subtract algebraic fractions in the same way as you add
and subtract numerical fractions.

> **example**
>
> Is this statement true or false? $\dfrac{1}{a} + \dfrac{1}{b} = \dfrac{2}{a+b}$
>
> ....
>
> False: $\dfrac{1}{a} + \dfrac{1}{b} = \dfrac{b}{ab} + \dfrac{a}{ab} = \dfrac{a+b}{ab}$

See N4 for adding fractions.

Exercise A1

L5

1 Simplify these expressions.
The first one has been done for you.
a $n + 4 + 5 = n + 9$
b $4n + 7n$
c $8n + 7 - 5n$

2 Simplify these expressions.

a $8 + 3f + 2f$ **b** $6g + 5 + 3g - 1$

3 This algebra chain begins and ends with $x + 3$.
Show what to do to move along each step in the chain.
The first step has been done for you.

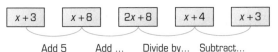

Add 5   Add ...   Divide by...   Subtract...

4 Amanda has a large pile of cards.
An expression for the total number of cards is $4n + 10$.

  a Amanda puts the cards into two piles.
    The number of cards in the first pile is $3n + 1$.
    Write an expression for the number of cards in the second pile.
  b Amanda puts the cards together and then puts them into two piles of equal size.
    Write an expression for the number of cards in each pile.

L6

5 Write each expression in its simplest form.

  a $(2a - 1) + (3a - 2)$ **b** $(3b + 5) - (b - 3)$ **c** $5c - (^-2c)$

6 A rectangle has sides n cm and 12 cm.

  a Write an expression for the perimeter of the rectangle.

  The rectangle is cut in half and the halves placed side by side.

  b What is the perimeter of the new rectangle?
    Write the expression as simply as possible.

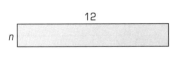

L7

7 Expand the brackets and simplify these expressions.

  a $3(5x + 3) - 2(2x + 1)$ **b** $4(x + 5) - 3(2 - x)$ **c** $2(3x - 1) - 3(4 - 2x)$
  d $(x + 2)(x + 4)$ **e** $(x + 5)(x - 2)$ **f** $(x + 3)^2$

8 Simplify:

  a $a^5 \times a^2$ **b** $ab^2 \times a^2$ **c** $2a^3b^2 \times 3a$ **d** $a^9 \div a^2$ **e** $8a^5 \div 2a^2$

9 Write these expression as simply as possible.

  a $4ab \times 3b^2$ **b** $\dfrac{5a^3b}{2ab}$

10 Simplify $\dfrac{1}{a} - \dfrac{1}{b}$.

11 In these walls each brick is made by adding the two bricks underneath it.
Copy the walls and fill in the missing expressions.
Write each expression as simply as possible.

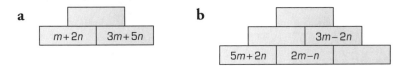

You can find a value for an expression by substituting numbers for letters. Use the correct order of operations.

▶ Work out brackets first.
▶ Next work out powers or roots.
▶ Then multiply or divide.
▶ Finally add or subtract.

example

Evaluate these expressions by substituting $x = 7$ and $y = 2$.

a $2x - 3y^2$ **b** $29 - (x + 2y) - y^3$

a $2x - 3y^2$
$= 2 \times 7 - 3 \times 2^2$
$= 14 - 12$
$= 2$

b $29 - (x + 2y) - y^3$
$= 29 - (7 + 2 \times 2) - 8$
$= 29 - 11 - 8$
$= 10$

An **equation** links two expressions with an equals sign.

▶ To solve an equation collect all letter terms on one side and number terms on the other side.

example

Solve:

a $3x + 7 = 22$ **b** $7x - 3 = 5x + 11$

a Subtract 7: $3x = 15$
   Divide by 3: $x = 5$

b Subtract $5x$: $2x - 3 = 11$
   Add 3: $2x = 14$
   Divide by 2: $x = 7$

You do the same to both sides of the equation.

You often need to form equations to solve problems.

example

This rectangle has a perimeter of 24 cm. Find x.

$x + 4$
$x - 1$

The perimeter is $2(x - 1 + x + 4) = 4x + 6$
$4x + 6 = 24$
$4x = 18$
$x = 4.5$ cm

Check your answer:
$4.5 - 1 = 3.5$
$4.5 + 4 = 8.5$
Perimeter $= (3.5 + 8.5) \times 2 = 24$

▶ A **formula** is a statement that relates two or more letters.

To change the subject of a formula you rearrange it so that a different letter is on its own.

example

Rearrange this equation to make F the subject.
$$C = \frac{5}{9}(F - 32)$$

Multiply by 9: $9C = 5(F - 32)$

Divide by 5: $\frac{9C}{5} = F - 32$

Add 32: $\frac{9C}{5} + 32 = F$

Changing the subject is like solving an equation – do the same to both sides.

Exercise A2

L5 M **1** When $x = 4$ work out the value of these expressions.
  a $5x + 3$ **b** $20 - 3x$ **c** $2x - 5$

M **2** When $x = 6$ work out the value of these expressions.
  a $2x + 7$ **b** $3x - 5$ **c** $6 + 5x$

3 Solve $4y + 11 = 35$ to find the value of y. Show your working.

4 Complete the missing values in this table.

x	$x - 1$	$3x$	$3(x - 1)$	$3x - 1$
5	4			
	9			
		18		

5 Mo has 4 full bags of sweets and 3 single sweets.
The number of sweets in each bag is the same.
  a Write an expression for the total number of sweets that Mo has,
    using n for the number of sweets inside each bag.
  b Ian thinks that the total number of sweets that Mo has is 24.
    Could Ian be correct? Explain how you know.

L6 **6** I think of a number.
Multiplying my number by four and adding one gives the same
answer as multiplying my number by three and adding five.
I call my number x and form an equation: $4x + 1 = 3x + 5$
Solve this equation and write down the value of x. Show your working.

7 I think of a number.
Doubling my number and adding seven gives the same answer as
multiplying my number by five and subtracting two.
  a Call the number x and form an equation.
  b Solve this equation and write down the value of x. Show your working.

8 Find x and y if:
  a $\frac{3}{5} = \frac{x}{20}$ **b** $\frac{2}{5} = \frac{7}{y}$

🖩 **9** When $x = 3.2$ and $y = 1.8$, work out the value of $(x + y)(x - y)$.

10 This is a square tile.
The edge of the tile is n cm long.
The perimeter of the tile is $4n$ cm.
This E-shape is made with 10 square tiles.
Write an expression for the perimeter of the E-shape.

11 Solve these equations. Show your working.
  a $3x + 4 = x + 1$ **b** $2(x + 3) = 14$

L7 **12** y is the subject of this equation. $y = 3(x + 4)$
Rearrange the equation to make x the subject.

13 Rearrange the equation $y = 2(a - x)$ to make x the subject. Show your working.

🖩 **14** $y = \pm\sqrt{\dfrac{x^2 + 1}{x}}$

  a When $x = 3$ calculate the positive value of y. Show all the digits on your calculator display.
  b When $x = 3$ give both values of y correct to 3 significant figures.

🖩 **15** Find the value of these expressions when $x = 4$.
  a $\dfrac{2(3 + x)^2}{x^2}$ **b** $\dfrac{3x(x - 1)}{5}$

When an equation is too complicated to solve you can find an approximate solution using trial and improvement.
Follow these steps:

KEYWORDS
Equation   Systematic
Substitute   Solution
Trial and improvement

▶ Estimate the solution and substitute it into the equation.
▶ Write down the value that you try and what you get when you substitute.
▶ Try to improve your estimate, using what you know from previous estimates.

> **example**
>
> Use trial and improvement to find an exact solution of $x^2 + x = 210$.
>
> | Try $x = 10$ | $10^2 + 10 = 110$ | too low |
> |---|---|---|
> | Try $x = 20$ | $20^2 + 20 = 420$ | too high |
> | Try $x = 15$ | $15^2 + 15 = 240$ | too high |
> | Try $x = 14$ | $14^2 + 14 = 210$ | ✓ |
>
> So $x = 14$ is one solution of the equation.

Using a table helps you to be systematic.

Some equations do not have exact solutions, so you have to give a rounded solution.

> **example**
>
> $y = x^2 - 5x + 3$
> There is a value of x between 0 and 1 that makes $y = 0$.
> There is also a value of x between 4 and 5 that makes $y = 0$.
> Find these values of x to 1 dp.
>
> | Try $x = 0.5$ | $y = 0.75$ | too high |
> |---|---|---|
> | Try $x = 0.6$ | $y = 0.36$ | too high |
> | Try $x = 0.7$ | $y = {}^-0.01$ | too low |
> | Try $x = 0.65$ | $y = 0.1725$ | too high |
>
> | Try $x = 4.2$ | $y = {}^-0.36$ | too low |
> |---|---|---|
> | Try $x = 4.3$ | $y = {}^-0.01$ | too low |
> | Try $x = 4.4$ | $y = 0.36$ | too high |
> | Try $x = 4.35$ | $y = 0.1725$ | too high |
>
> x is between 0.65 and 0.7
> so $x = 0.7$ to 1 dp.
>
> x is between 4.3 and 4.35
> so $x = 4.3$ to 1 dp.

Once you know x is between 0.6 and 0.7, check the halfway value to see which is the best estimate.

Approximate solutions can also be found from a graph.

You can read off the solutions at $y = 0$ (where the graph cuts the x-axis).

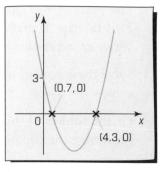

> **example**
>
> Use trial and improvement to estimate $\sqrt{1000}$ to 2 dp.
>
> Form the equation: $x^2 = 1000$
>
> | Try $x = 31.5$ | $31.5^2 = 992.25$ | too low |
> |---|---|---|
> | Try $x = 31.65$ | $31.65^2 = 1001.72$ | too high |
> | Try $x = 31.63$ | $31.63^2 = 1000.46$ | too high |
> | Try $x = 31.62$ | $31.62^2 = 999.82$ | too low |
>
> So $\sqrt{1000} = 31.62$ to 2 dp.

Exercise A3

L5 **1** **a** Two numbers multiply together to make ⁻24.
   They add together to make 5.
   What are the two numbers?
   b Two numbers multiply together to make ⁻24.
   They add together to make ⁻5.
   What are the two numbers?
   c Two numbers multiply together to make 18.
   They add together to make ⁻9.
   What are the two numbers?

L6 **2** Students started to solve the equation $5x + 2 = 8x - 11$ in different ways.

   a Whose statement is correct?

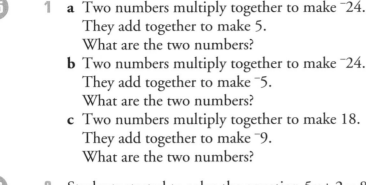

Saeed
$5x + 2 = 8x - 11$
so $7x = ⁻3x$

Gareth
$5x + 2 = 8x - 11$
so $13x = 13$

Ama
$5x + 2 = 8x - 11$
so $3x = 13$

   b Another student used trial and improvement to solve the equation
   $5x + 2 = 8x - 11$.
   Explain why trial and improvement is not a good method to use.

L7 **3** The table shows values of x and y for the equation $y = x^2 + x - 1$.

   a Copy and complete the table.

x	⁻3	⁻2	⁻1	0	1	2	3
y	5	1	⁻1	⁻1	1		

   The value of y is 0 for a value of x between 0 and 1 and another
   value of x between ⁻2 and ⁻1.
   b Use trial and improvement to find these values of x to one decimal place.

x	y
0	⁻1
1	1

x	y
⁻2	1
⁻1	⁻1

4 James wants to find a value for x such that $x^3 = 4 + x$.
   The table shows that the value of x lies between 1 and 2.

x	x^3	$4 + x$
1	1	5
2	8	6

   Use trial and improvement to find the value of x correct to one decimal place.

5 The stopping distance of a car can be estimated using the formula

   $$D = \frac{S^2 + 3S}{25}$$

   where S is the speed of the car in km/h and D is the stopping distance in m.

   a After an accident skid marks 60 m long were measured on
   the road.
   The table shows the car was travelling at a speed between
   30 and 40 km/h.
   Find an estimate for the speed of the car correct to the nearest 1 km/h.

S	20	30	40
$D = \frac{S^2 + 3S}{25}$	18.4	39.6	68.8

   b In a second accident skid marks 100 m long were measured on the road.
   Find an estimate for the speed of the car correct to the nearest 1 km/h for this accident.

L5

(A1)

1 a It is Tina's birthday. We do not know how old Tina is.
Call **Tina's age**, in years, n.
The expressions below compare Tina's age to some other people's ages.
Use words to compare their ages. The first one is done for you.

i

Tina's age	n
Ann's age	$n+3$

Ann is   *3 years older than Tina.*

ii

Tina's age	n
Barry's age	$n-1$

iii

Tina's age	n
Carol's age	$2n$

b In one year's time Tina's age will be $n+1$.
Copy and complete the table to show the ages of the other people in one year's time.

	Tina	Ann	Barry	Carol
Age now	n	$n+3$	$n-1$	$2n$
Age in one year's time	$n+1$			

c i When $n=30$, find the value of $2n+1$.
 ii When $n=30$, find the value of $2(n+1)$.

2 Copy the diagram.
Match each expression with the correct number when $x=6$.

(A2)

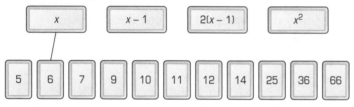

| x | $x-1$ | $2(x-1)$ | x^2 |

| 5 | 6 | 7 | 9 | 10 | 11 | 12 | 14 | 25 | 36 | 66 |

L6

3 a The diagram shows a rectangle. Its dimensions are $3a$ by $5b$.

(A1)

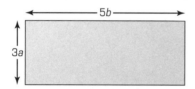

Write **simplified expressions** for the area and the perimeter of this rectangle.
 b A different rectangle has **area $12a^2$** and **perimeter $14a$**.
What are the dimensions of this rectangle?

4 Three people play a game with counters.
Each person starts with some bags of counters.
Each bag has m counters in it.
The table shows what happened during the game.

(A2)

	Start	During game	End of game
Lisa	3 bags	lost 5 counters	$3m-5$
Ben	2 bags	won 3 counters	$2m+3$
Maria	4 bags	won 2 counters	$4m+2$

 a At the end of the game, **Lisa** and **Ben** had the **same** number of counters.
Write an **equation** to show this.
 b Solve the equation to find m, the number of counters in each bag at the start of the game.

L6

5 A drink from a machine costs **55p**.
The table shows the coins that were put into the machine one day.

N8

Coins	Number of coins
50p	31
20p	22
10p	41
5p	59

How many cans of drink were sold that day?
Show your working.

6 Find the values of t and r in these equations.

A2

a $\dfrac{2}{3} = \dfrac{t}{6}$ 　　　　**b** $\dfrac{2}{3} = \dfrac{5}{r}$

L7

7 The ship 'Queen Mary' used to sail across the Atlantic Ocean.
The ship's usual speed was **33 miles per hour**.
On average, the ship used fuel at the rate of **1 gallon** for every **13 feet** sailed.

N9

a Calculate how many gallons of fuel the ship used in one hour of travelling at the usual speed. (There are 5280 feet in one mile.)
Show your working and write down the **full calculator display**.

b Now write your answer correct to **2 significant figures**.

8 a Find the values of a and b in each formula when $p = 10$.

A2

　　i 　$a = \dfrac{3p^3}{2}$

　　ii 　$b = \dfrac{2p^2(p-3)}{7p}$

b Simplify this expression as fully as possible: $\dfrac{3cd^2}{5cd}$

A1

c Multiply out and simplify these expressions:

A1

　　i 　$3(x-2) - 2(4-3x)$
　　ii 　$(x+2)(x+3)$
　　iii 　$(x+4)(x-1)$
　　iv 　$(x-2)^2$

9 For each part of the question, write down the statement that is true.

A1

a **i** When x is even, $(x-2)^2$ is even.
　　ii When x is even, $(x-2)^2$ is odd.
　　Show how you know it is true for **all** even values of x.

b **i** When x is even, $(x-1)(x+1)$ is even.
　　ii When x is even, $(x-1)(x+1)$ is odd.
　　Show how you know it is true for **all** even values of x.

10 The table below shows values of x and y for the equation $y = x^2 + x - 5$.

A3

a Copy and complete the table.

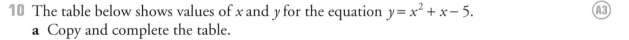

x	-2	-1	0	1	2	3
y				-3	1	7

The value of y is 0 for a value of x between 1 and 2.

b Find the value of x, to 1 decimal place, that gives the value of y closest to 0.
You may use trial and improvement.

A **sequence** is a set of numbers, patterns or terms that follow a rule.
A **linear** or **arithmetic sequence** increases by the same amount each time.

▶ You can generate terms of a sequence using
  ▷ a term-to-term rule and a term, or
  ▷ a position-to-term rule.

example

Find the next two terms of this sequence: 3, 6, 12, 24, ...

The terms are doubled each time, so the next two terms are 48 and 96.

'Terms are doubled each time' is a term-to-term rule.

The *n*th term can be used to describe a sequence.
If the *n*th term of a sequence is $4n - 1$, substituting $n = 1, 2, 3, 4, ...$
gives the sequence 3, 7, 10, 13.

example

This is the sequence of triangle numbers:

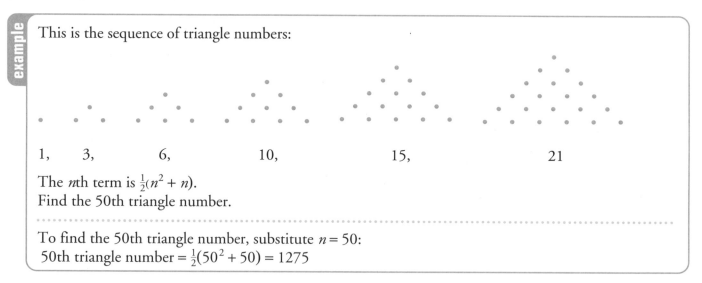

1,   3,   6,   10,   15,   21

The *n*th term is $\frac{1}{2}(n^2 + n)$.
Find the 50th triangle number.

To find the 50th triangle number, substitute $n = 50$:
50th triangle number $= \frac{1}{2}(50^2 + 50) = 1275$

You can use differences between terms to find the *n*th term of a sequence.

▶ A **linear sequence** has a constant first difference pattern.

This is a linear sequence as the first difference is always 2:

5,   7,   9,   11, ...
  +2   +2   +2

As the difference is 2, the *n*th term will be '$2n +$ something'.
The first term ($n = 1$) is $2 \times 1 + 3$ so in this case the general term is $2n + 3$.

$2n + 3$ is a position-to-term rule.

▶ A **quadratic sequence** has a constant second difference pattern.

The *n*th term of a quadratic sequence will have highest power n^2.

example

Find the *n*th term of this sequence.

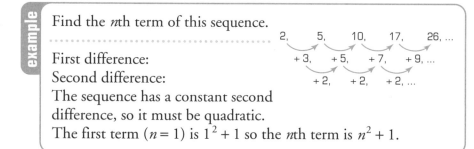

2,   5,   10,   17,   26, ...
First difference:
  +3,   +5,   +7,   +9, ...
Second difference:
  +2,   +2,   +2, ...

The sequence has a constant second
difference, so it must be quadratic.
The first term ($n = 1$) is $1^2 + 1$ so the *n*th term is $n^2 + 1$.

Check:
When $n = 2$,
$n^2 + 1 = 2^2 + 1 = 5$

Exercise A4

L5

1 Here is a number chain: $5 \rightarrow 7 \rightarrow 9 \rightarrow 11 \rightarrow 13$
The rule is: Add 2

   a A different number chain is: $5 \rightarrow 10 \rightarrow 20 \rightarrow 40$
   What could the rule be?
   b Some number chains start like this: $3 \rightarrow 6 \rightarrow$
   Show three different ways to continue this number chain.
   Write down the rule you are using each time.

2 You can make hexagon rows with matchsticks.

| 1 hexagon | 2 hexagons | 3 hexagons |
| 6 matchsticks | 11 matchsticks | 16 matchsticks |

   a How many matchsticks will be needed for a row of 4 hexagons?
   b The rule for finding the number of matchsticks is:
   5 times the number of hexagons add 1.
   Use the rule to find out how many matchsticks are needed for
   a row of 11 hexagons.
   c M = number of matchsticks and H = number of hexagons.
   Write down the rule connecting M and H.

L6

3 A pattern is made from black and white tiles.

   a How many black tiles and how many white tiles will
   there be in

   i pattern 6   **ii** pattern 10   **iii** pattern P?

   b T = total number of black and white tiles and P = pattern number.
   Write an equation connecting T and P.

Pattern   1   2   3

4 For each of the following sequences:

   i Write down the next two terms.
   ii Find a rule for the nth term.

   a 6, 11, 16, 21, ...   **b** 9, 16, 23, 30, ...   **c** 1, 5, 9, 13, ...

L7

5 Look at this number line.

   a Fill in the two missing numbers.
   b Copy and complete this sentence:
   The numbers on this number line go up in steps of _____

6 Sammy is using square patterns of dots to find expressions for n^2.
$3^2 = 2^2 + 2 + 3$ $4^2 = 3^2 + 3 + 4$ $5^2 = 4^2 + 4 + 5$

Sammy wants to write an expression for n^2 using her diagrams.
Write down Sammy's expression for n^2: $n^2 = $ _____

31

You can draw a graph by substituting values of x into the equation to find corresponding values of y. Plot and join the (x, y) points.

KEYWORDS
Equation   Graph
Gradient   Intercept
Simultaneous equations

example

Draw these lines.
a $y = x$ **b** $y = 2x$ **c** $y = 3x - 1$ **d** $x + y = 5$

Generate at least three points for each graph:

x	$^-1$	0	1
a $y = x$	$^-1$	0	1
b $y = 2x$	$^-2$	0	2
c $y = 3x - 1$	$^-4$	$^-1$	2
d $x + y = 5$	6	5	4

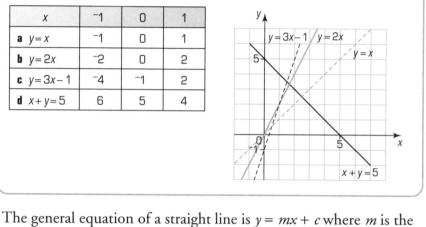

You should be able to draw horizontal lines like $y = 4$ and vertical lines like $x = 2$ without drawing a table of values:

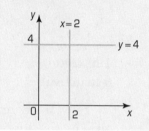

▶ The general equation of a straight line is $y = mx + c$ where m is the gradient of the line and c is the y-intercept.
A line with gradient 3 and y-intercept 2 has equation $y = 3x + 2$.

The y-intercept is where the line crosses the y-axis.

example

State the gradient and y-intercept for these lines:
a $y = x$ **b** $y = 2x$ **c** $y = 3x - 1$ **d** $x + y = 5$

a $y = x$: $m = 1$, $c = 0$
b $y = 2x$: $m = 2$, $c = 0$
c $y = 3x - 1$: $m = 3$, $c = {}^-1$
d $x + y = 5$ so $y = {}^-x + 5$: $m = {}^-1$, $c = 5$

For part **d** you need to rearrange the equation to the form $y = mx + c$.

Simultaneous equations are equations that are true at the same time. To solve simultaneous equations you find values for the unknowns that satisfy both equations. This is the point where their graphs intersect.

example

Solve these simultaneous equations: $x + y = 6$
                                         $y = 2x + 3$

The lines meet at $(1, 5)$ so the solution is $x = 1$, $y = 5$.

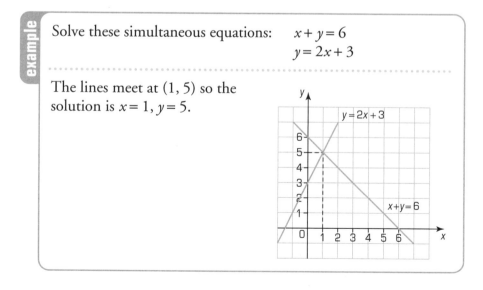

Exercise A5

L5 1 You pay £3.60 each time you visit the gym.

a Copy and complete the table.

Number of gym visits	0	5	10	15
Total cost (£)	0			

b Show this information on a graph.
Join the points with a straight line.

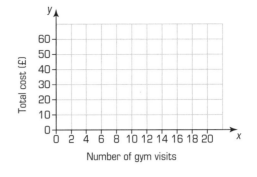

c A different way to pay is to pay a monthly fee of £18.
Then you pay £1.60 each time you visit the gym.

Copy and complete the table.

Number of gym visits	0	5	10	15
Total cost (£)	18			

d Show this information on the same graph.
Join the points with a straight line.

e For how many visits to the gym does the graph show that the cost is the same for both ways of paying?

L6 2 Sketch the graphs of:
a $y = x$ b $y = 4$ c $x = {}^-1$

3 Does the point $(20, 40)$ lie on the line $y = 2x$?
Explain how you know.

4 Look at this diagram.

a The line through points A and B has equation $y = 0$.
What is the equation of the line through C and E?
b The line through the points A and E has equation $x + y = 1$.
What is the equation of the line through B and D?

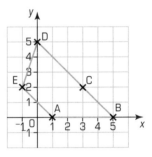

L7 5 Draw the graphs of:
a $x + y = 6$ b $y = 2x + 1$

6 Here are five equations. Think about the graphs of these equations.

A $y = 2x + 3$ **B** $y = x^3$ **C** $y = 2x - 3$ **D** $x = 2$ **E** $y = 2$

a Which two graphs go through the point $(2, 2)$?
b Which graph is parallel to the x-axis?
c Which graph is not a straight line?
d Which graphs have the same gradient?

7 a On the same graph draw the lines $y = 3x - 1$ and $y = x + 4$.
Use axes from 0 to 8.
b Use your graph to solve these simultaneous equations:
$y = 3x - 1$
$y = x + 4$

8 a On the same graph draw the lines $y = 3x - 8$ and $y = 7 - 2x$.
Use axes from 0 to 6.
b Use your graph to solve these simultaneous equations:
$y = 3x - 8$
$y = 7 - 2x$

A6 Real-life graphs

An inequality is a relationship between two terms that are not equal.

    < means 'less than'   > means 'greater than'

▶ An inequality has a range of values as its solution.
    The integer values that satisfy the inequality $x > 3$ are $x = 4, 5, 6, 7, ...$

An integer is a positive or negative whole number.

You can represent information on a graph to solve problems.

example

Companies charge different amounts for using mobile phones.
The graph shows the amounts charged by two companies.

a Find the missing numbers from these sentences:
Company A: You pay £___ every month, then 10p per minute.
Company B: You pay ___ p every minute.

b For how long do both companies charge the same?

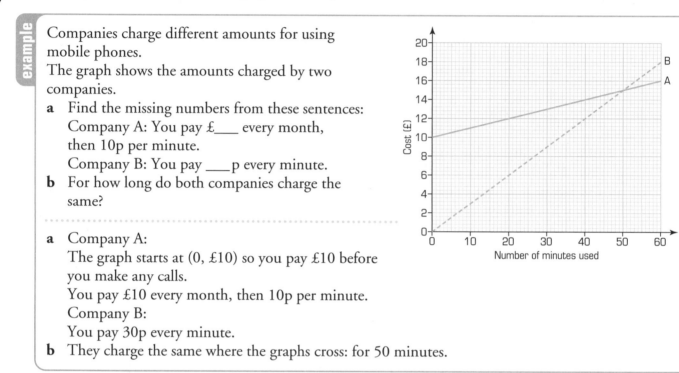

- -

a Company A:
The graph starts at (0, £10) so you pay £10 before you make any calls.
You pay £10 every month, then 10p per minute.
Company B:
You pay 30p every minute.

b They charge the same where the graphs cross: for 50 minutes.

Distance–time graphs can be used to show journeys.

example

This graph shows a cyclist's journey.

a When does the cyclist stop for a rest?
How can you tell?

b How far away from home is the cyclist after 20 minutes?

c What is the greatest speed?

d Why does the graph slope downwards after 55 minutes?

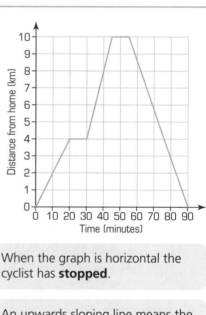

- -

a The cyclist is resting at 20–30 minutes and 45–55 minutes, because the graph is horizontal.

b 4 km

c The greatest speed is where the graph is steepest:

$$\text{Speed} = \frac{\text{distance travelled}}{\text{time taken}}$$

$\text{Speed} = 6\ \text{km} \div \frac{1}{4}\ \text{h} = 24\ \text{km/h}$

d The cyclist is returning home.

When the graph is horizontal the cyclist has **stopped**.

An upwards sloping line means the cyclist is moving **away** from where he started.

A downwards sloping line means he is returning **towards** where he started.

Exercise A6

L5

1 A cookery book shows the cooking temperatures in degrees Fahrenheit.
This graph can be used to convert degrees Fahrenheit to degrees Celsius.

Use the graph to convert these temperatures to °C.

a 320 °F **b** 280 °F **c** 350 °F

Give sensible answers.

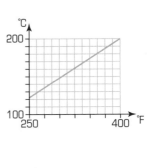

L6

2 Mobile phone providers have different tariffs for calls.
The graph shows monthly call charges for two different price plans.

a How much would you pay if you made 50 minutes of calls on price plan A?

b If one month you were charged £12.50 on price plan B, for how many minutes would you have used the mobile phone in that month?

c Copy and complete these sentences.

   i On price plan A you pay _____ for each minute of calls.

   ii On price plan B you pay _____ plus _____ for each minute of calls.

d When would it be cheaper to be on price plan B instead of price plan A?

L7 **M**

3 Look at this inequality. $3 \leqslant x < 7$
Write down all the integer solutions.

M

4 Look at this inequality. $^-3 < x \leqslant 8.5$
Write down all the integer solutions.

5 a

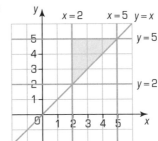

One region can be described by the inequalities:

$$y \leqslant x \quad y \leqslant 4 \quad y \geqslant 3 \quad x \leqslant 4$$

Copy the graph and shade the region described.

b

The shaded region can be described by three inequalities.
Write down these inequalities.

6 The graph shows the depth of water in a bath.
From A to B both taps are turned full on.

a At what time did someone get into the bath?
b When were the taps turned off?
c How long did it take for the bath water to empty out?

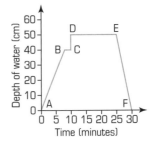

35

Angles and triangles

You should learn these angle facts:

▶ Angles on a straight line add to 180°.

▶ Angles around a point add to 360°.

▶ Angles in a triangle add to 180°.

▶ Angles in a quadrilateral add to 360°.

▶ Exterior angle of a triangle = sum of two interior opposite angles

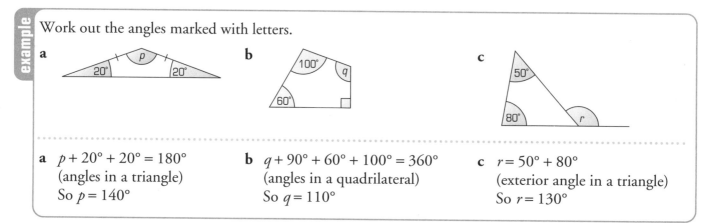

$x = y + z$

You should give reasons for your answers.

example

Work out the angles marked with letters.

a   **b**   **c**

a $p + 20° + 20° = 180°$
(angles in a triangle)
So $p = 140°$

b $q + 90° + 60° + 100° = 360°$
(angles in a quadrilateral)
So $q = 110°$

c $r = 50° + 80°$
(exterior angle in a triangle)
So $r = 130°$

Angles are formed when lines cross.
You should learn these three angle facts:

Vertically opposite angles are equal.

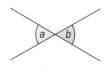

$a = b$

Alternate angles are equal.

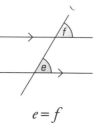

$c = d$

Corresponding angles are equal.

$e = f$

example

Work out the angles marked with letters.

a   **b**   **c**

a $s = 55°$
(vertically opposite angles)

b $t = 30°$
(alternate angles)

c $u = 45°$
(corresponding angles)

KEYWORDS
Quadrilateral   Corresponding
Alternate   Triangle
Vertically opposite

Exercise S1

L5

1 Eddie and Steve measured this angle.
Eddie said it was 253°.
Steve said it was 107°.
Explain why they could both be correct.

2 What is the missing angle *a*?

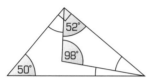

Explain how you found the answer.

L6

3 Two shapes fit together to make a right-angled triangle.

Find the size of the three missing angles.

4 Calculate angles *a*, *b*, *c* and *d*.

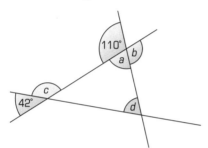

Explain how you found each angle.

5 Angie draws a parallelogram.

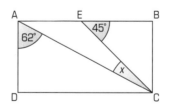

Calculate the angles *x* and *y*.

L7

6 ABCD is a rectangle.
Find angle *x*.
Explain how you found your answer.

7 This star has rotational symmetry of order 5.

Find angles *x* and *y*.

8 A rectangle is shown resting on a triangle.
Find angle *x*.

37

A **polygon** is a closed shape with three or more straight sides.

Pentagon

5 sides

Hexagon

6 sides

Octagon

8 sides

KEYWORDS

Polygon	Hexagon
Pentagon	Rhombus
Octagon	Trapezium
Parallelogram	Isosceles
Equilateral	

An **exterior angle** of a polygon is formed by extending one of the sides.

exterior
angle

You should learn these polygon angle facts:

▶ The sum of the exterior angles of any polygon is 360°.

▶ An exterior angle of a regular n-sided polygon = $360 \div n$.

Regular shapes have equal angles and sides.

▶ An interior angle = 180° − exterior angle

▶ The sum of the interior angles of a regular n-sided polygon = interior angle × n

example

Find the sum of the interior angles of a decagon (a 10-sided polygon).

....

Exterior angle = 360 ÷ 10 = 36°
Interior angle = 180 − 36 = 144°
Sum interior angles = 144 × 10 = 1440°

You should know the properties of these special triangles:

Right-angled
One 90° angle

Isosceles
Two angles equal
Two sides equal

Equilateral
All three angles equal
All three sides equal

You should know the properties of these special quadrilaterals:

Square
Two pairs of parallel sides
All sides equal

Rectangle
Two pairs of parallel sides
Opposite sides equal

Kite
Adjacent sides equal

Trapezium
One pair of parallel sides

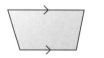

Parallelogram
Two pairs of parallel sides
Opposite sides equal

Rhombus
Two pairs of parallel sides
All sides equal

Exercise S2

L5

1 WY is a line of symmetry.
Copy and complete the following:
WZ is _____ long.
WX is _____ long.
The angle at X is equal to the angle at _____

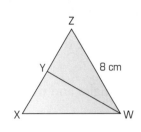

2 On this square grid points A and B cannot move.
When C is at (4, 3) ABC is an isosceles triangle.

    a C moves so that ABC is still an isosceles triangle.
    Write down the coordinates of a position that C could move to.
    b C moves so that triangle ABC is isosceles and right-angled.
    Write down the coordinates of a position that C could move to.

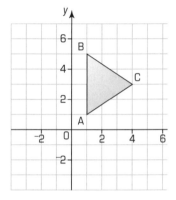

L6

3 This is an isosceles triangle.

    a If angle $x = 20°$, work out angle y.
    b If angle $y = 20°$, work out angle x.

4 A pentagon can be split into three triangles.

    a Explain how you know the angles inside a pentagon add up to 540°.

    b What do the angles inside a hexagon add up to?
    Explain how you know.

    c What do the angles inside a decagon add up to?

5 The angles inside an octagon add up to 1080°.

    a Work out the size of one interior angle of a regular octagon.
    b Work out the size of one exterior angle of a regular octagon.

6 Here is a parallelogram.

    a What would you change on the parallelogram to turn it into a rhombus?
    b What would you change on the parallelogram to turn it into a rectangle?

L7

7 The diagram shows an equilateral triangle ABF.
CDEF is a rectangle.
ABC and AFE are straight lines.

Show that BCF is an isosceles triangle.

8 This pattern has rotational symmetry of order 5.

    a What is the size of angle y?
    Show your working.

Each quadrilateral shown in the diagram is made
from two identical isosceles triangles.
    b What is the special name of this quadrilateral?
    c Work out the size of angle z.

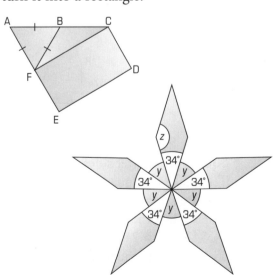

▶ Shapes are **similar** if their angles are the same and their sides are in the same ratio.

▶ Shapes are **congruent** if their angles and their sides are exactly the same.

example

These shapes are similar.
Find side *x*.

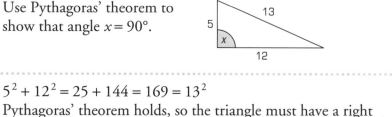

All equilateral triangles are similar.

Side *x* corresponds to the side of length 3 cm.
The side of length 9 cm corresponds to the side of length 4 cm.

So $\dfrac{x}{3} = \dfrac{9}{4}$, rearranging gives $x = \dfrac{9 \times 3}{4}$

So $x = 6.75$ cm

Pythagoras' theorem can help you work out the lengths of sides in right-angled triangles.

▶ In a right-angled triangle with sides *a*, *b*, *c* where *c* is the hypotenuse:

$$a^2 + b^2 = c^2$$

The **hypotenuse** is the longest side. It is opposite the right angle.

▶ To find the hypotenuse:
square the other two sides, add them and then take the square root.

▶ To find a shorter side:
square the other two sides, subtract and then take the square root.

example

Use Pythagoras' theorem to show that angle $x = 90°$.

$5^2 + 12^2 = 25 + 144 = 169 = 13^2$
Pythagoras' theorem holds, so the triangle must have a right angle opposite the longest side: $x = 90°$.

example

a Find length PR.
b Find length RS.

a You are looking for the hypotenuse in triangle PQR.
Square the shorter sides and add: $6^2 + 8^2 = 36 + 64 = 100$.
Then take the square root: $\sqrt{100} = 10$ cm, so PR = 10 cm.
b You are looking for a shorter side in triangle PRS.
Square the other sides and subtract:
$14.5^2 - 10^2 = 210.25 - 100 = 110.25$
Then take the square root: $\sqrt{110.25} = 10.5$, so RS = 10.5 cm.

A sketch can help:

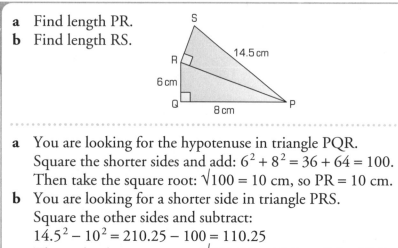

Exercise S3

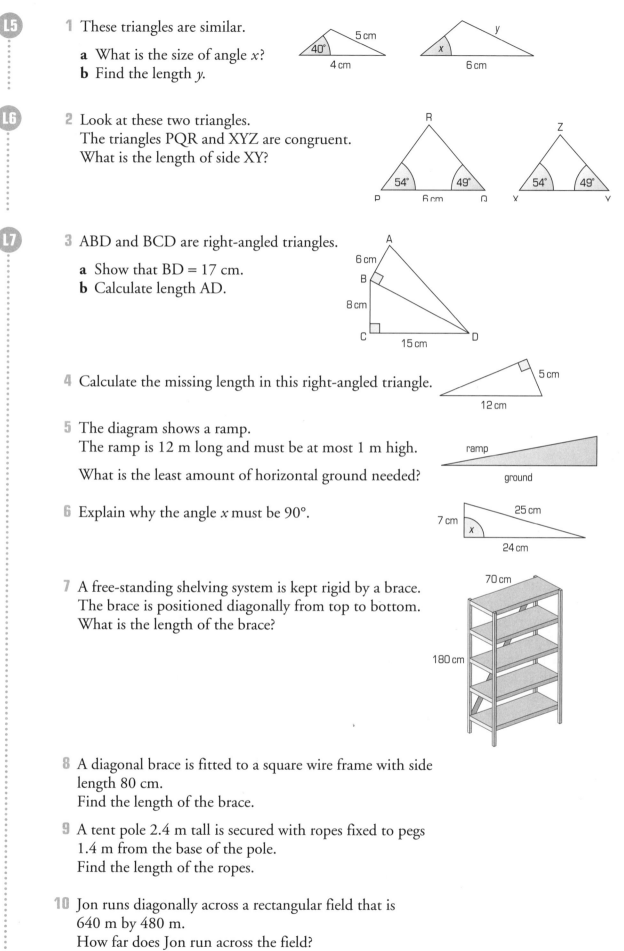

L5

1 These triangles are similar.

    a What is the size of angle *x*?
    b Find the length *y*.

5 cm
40°
4 cm
y
x
6 cm

L6

2 Look at these two triangles.
The triangles PQR and XYZ are congruent.
What is the length of side XY?

R
54°   49°
P   6 cm   Q
Z
54°   49°
X   Y

L7

3 ABD and BCD are right-angled triangles.

    a Show that BD = 17 cm.
    b Calculate length AD.

A
6 cm
B
8 cm
C   15 cm   D

4 Calculate the missing length in this right-angled triangle.

5 cm
12 cm

5 The diagram shows a ramp.
The ramp is 12 m long and must be at most 1 m high.

What is the least amount of horizontal ground needed?

ramp
ground

6 Explain why the angle *x* must be 90°.

25 cm
7 cm   *x*
24 cm

7 A free-standing shelving system is kept rigid by a brace.
The brace is positioned diagonally from top to bottom.
What is the length of the brace?

70 cm
180 cm

8 A diagonal brace is fitted to a square wire frame with side
length 80 cm.
Find the length of the brace.

9 A tent pole 2.4 m tall is secured with ropes fixed to pegs
1.4 m from the base of the pole.
Find the length of the ropes.

10 Jon runs diagonally across a rectangular field that is
640 m by 480 m.
How far does Jon run across the field?

L5

1 Steve is making a series of patterns with black and blue square tiles.

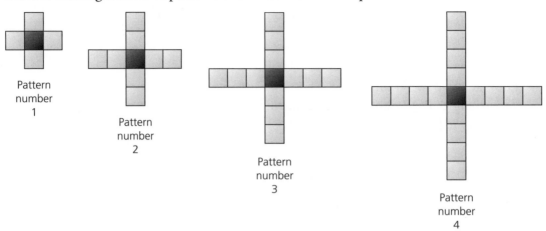

Pattern
number
1

Pattern
number
2

Pattern
number
3

Pattern
number
4

a Each pattern has **1 black tile** at the **centre**.
Each **new** pattern has **more blue tiles** that the one before.
How many **more** blue tiles does Steve add each time he makes
a new pattern?

b Steve says: 'The rule for finding the number of tiles in pattern
number N is: **number of tiles = 4 × N + 1**.'
The **1** in Steve's rule represents the **black tile**.
What does the **4 × N** represent?

c Steve wants to make **pattern number 15**.
How many **black** tiles and how many **blue** tiles does he need?

d Steve uses **41 tiles** altogether to make a pattern.
What is the number of the pattern he makes?

e Steve has **12 black** tiles and **80 blue** tiles.
What is the number of the **biggest** pattern Steve can make?

L6

2 Look at this diagram.

a The line through points A and F has
the equation $y = 11$.
What is the equation of the line
through points **A** and **B**?

b The line through points A and D
has the equation $y = x + 3$.
What is the equation of the line
through points **F** and **E**?

c What is the equation of the line
through points **B** and **C**?

A5

3 This shape has **3 identical white** tiles and **3
identical blue** tiles.
The sides of each tile are all the same length.
Opposite sides of each tile are parallel.
One of the angles is 70°.

a Calculate the size of **angle k**.

b Calculate the size of **angle m**.
Show your working.

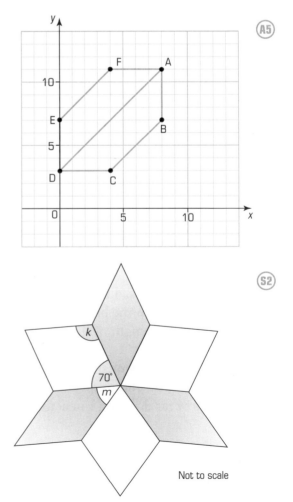

Not to scale

S2

L6

4 The diagram shows two isosceles triangles inside a parallelogram.

   a Write down another angle that is 75°.
   b Calculate the size of the angle marked *k*. Show your working.

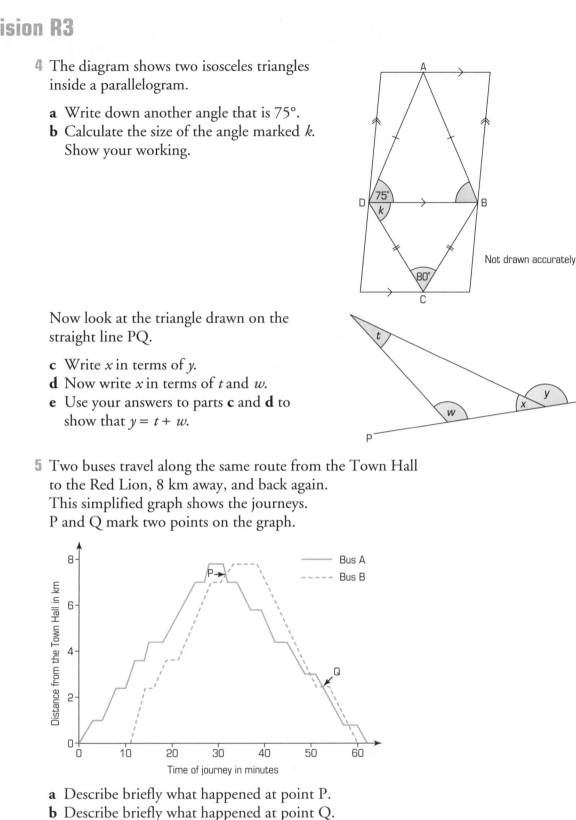

Not drawn accurately

Now look at the triangle drawn on the straight line PQ.

   c Write *x* in terms of *y*.
   d Now write *x* in terms of *t* and *w*.
   e Use your answers to parts **c** and **d** to show that $y = t + w$.

L7

5 Two buses travel along the same route from the Town Hall to the Red Lion, 8 km away, and back again. This simplified graph shows the journeys. P and Q mark two points on the graph.

   a Describe briefly what happened at point P.
   b Describe briefly what happened at point Q.

Bus A took 27 minutes to get to the Red Lion.
   c Work out the average speed in km per hour.
   d Bus B went at an average speed of 21.5 km per hour back to the Town Hall. Work out the average speed in **miles per hour**. Show your working.

6 A boat sails from the harbour to the buoy. The buoy is 6 km to the east and 4 km to the north of the harbour. **Calculate** the shortest distance between the buoy and the harbour. Give your answer to 1 decimal place. Show your working.

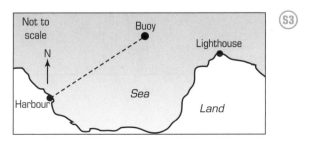

▶ You can use **isometric** paper to help you draw 3-D solids.

Here are three different views of the same solid drawn on isometric paper.

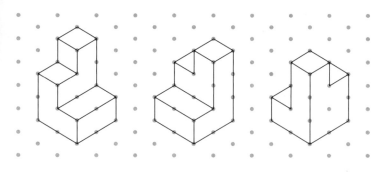

KEYWORDS
Isometric
Plan
Elevation

Make sure you have isometric paper the correct way up.
The vertical dots should be close together.

▶ **Plans** and **elevations** are projections of a 3-D solid onto a 2-D surface.
  ▷ A **plan** of a solid is the view from directly overhead (bird's-eye view).
  ▷ An **elevation** is the view from the front or the side of a solid.

Here are the plan and front and side elevations for the 3-D shape above.

Plan   Front elevation   Side elevation

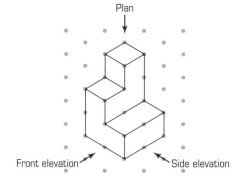

Plan

Front elevation →   ← Side elevation

---

example

Draw the plan, front and side elevations of this shape.

Plan   Front elevation   Side elevation

L5   **1**   On isometric paper like this draw a cuboid 5 squares by 4 squares by 3 squares.

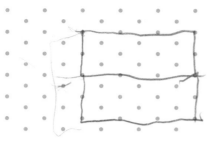

2   The diagram shows one view of a solid made up from 5 cubes.
Copy and complete the second diagram to show the same solid from a different view.

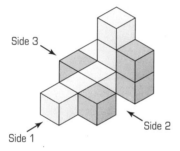

L6   **3**   The diagram shows a model made from 11 cubes.

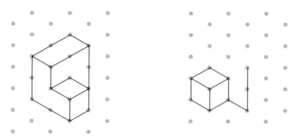

a   The drawings below show different side views of the model.
Which side view does each drawing show?

  i   **ii**   **iii**

b Draw the plan of the model.

4   The diagram shows an incomplete drawing
of a solid cube.
Copy the diagram and add 3 straight lines
to complete the drawing.

5   Lewis made a solid L-shape using 4 cubes.
He drew a picture of the L on a square grid.
He did not draw any side he could not see.

He rotated the solid through 180° so that it was upside-down.
Draw what the solid will look like on isometric paper.

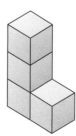

45

▶ A **net** is a 2-D arrangement that can be folded to form a solid shape.

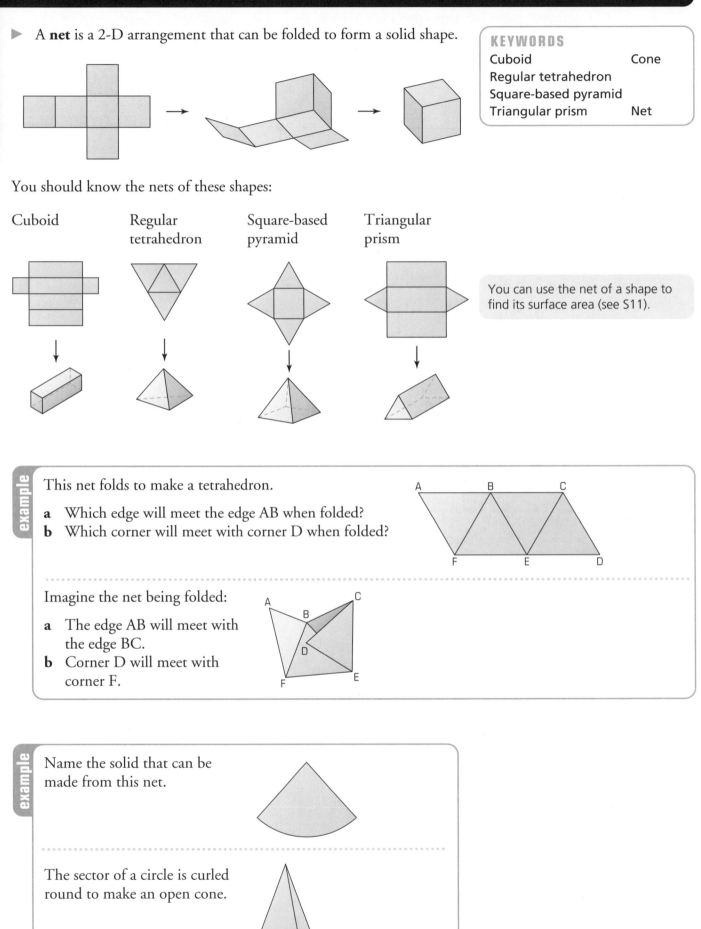

KEYWORDS

Cuboid	Cone
Regular tetrahedron	
Square-based pyramid	
Triangular prism	Net

You should know the nets of these shapes:

Cuboid   Regular tetrahedron   Square-based pyramid   Triangular prism

You can use the net of a shape to find its surface area (see S11).

example

This net folds to make a tetrahedron.

a Which edge will meet the edge AB when folded?
b Which corner will meet with corner D when folded?

Imagine the net being folded:

a The edge AB will meet with the edge BC.
b Corner D will meet with corner F.

example

Name the solid that can be made from this net.

The sector of a circle is curled round to make an open cone.

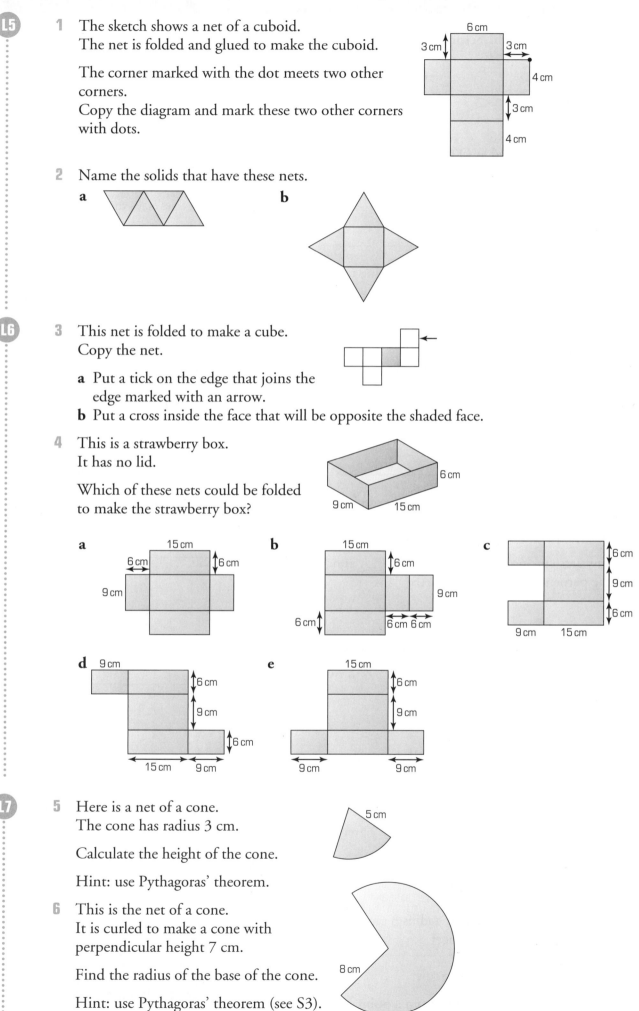

L5

1 The sketch shows a net of a cuboid.
The net is folded and glued to make the cuboid.

The corner marked with the dot meets two other corners.
Copy the diagram and mark these two other corners with dots.

2 Name the solids that have these nets.

a   **b**

L6

3 This net is folded to make a cube.
Copy the net.

a Put a tick on the edge that joins the edge marked with an arrow.
b Put a cross inside the face that will be opposite the shaded face.

4 This is a strawberry box.
It has no lid.

Which of these nets could be folded to make the strawberry box?

a **b** **c**

d **e**

L7

5 Here is a net of a cone.
The cone has radius 3 cm.

Calculate the height of the cone.

Hint: use Pythagoras' theorem.

6 This is the net of a cone.
It is curled to make a cone with perpendicular height 7 cm.

Find the radius of the base of the cone.

Hint: use Pythagoras' theorem (see S3).

You can construct an **angle bisector** using only a ruler and compasses.

KEYWORDS
Compasses   Locus
Bisect   Arc
Perpendicular

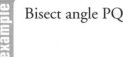

example

Bisect angle PQR.

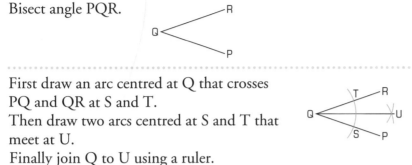

Bisect means split into two equal parts.

First draw an arc centred at Q that crosses PQ and QR at S and T.
Then draw two arcs centred at S and T that meet at U.
Finally join Q to U using a ruler.

Always leave the construction lines.

You construct the **perpendicular bisector** of a line using a ruler and compasses.

example

Find the perpendicular bisector of AB.

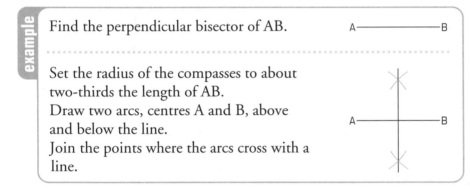

Perpendicular means at right angles to.

Set the radius of the compasses to about two-thirds the length of AB.
Draw two arcs, centres A and B, above and below the line.
Join the points where the arcs cross with a line.

The perpendicular bisector of AB is the locus of all points equidistant from A and B.

Equidistant means at an equal distance.

Here are some other constructions that you should know.

To construct a perpendicular from a point X *to* a line YZ:

▶ At X draw arcs cutting line YZ in two places, A and B.
▶ Draw the perpendicular bisector of AB.

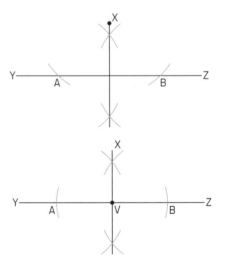

To construct a perpendicular from a point V *on* a line YZ:

▶ Draw an arc centred at V that cuts the line YZ in two places, A and B.
▶ Draw the perpendicular bisector of AB.

You can also construct a triangle given all three sides.

example

Construct a triangle of sides 3 cm, 5 cm and 6 cm.

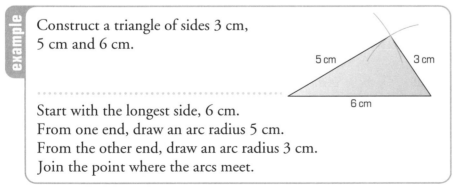

To construct an equilateral triangle you construct an angle of 60°.

Start with the longest side, 6 cm.
From one end, draw an arc radius 5 cm.
From the other end, draw an arc radius 3 cm.
Join the point where the arcs meet.

Hint: always sketch the diagram first.

A locus is a set of points that follow a rule.

▶ The locus of all points equidistant from a point is a circle.

The circumference is always the same distance from the centre.

Exercise S6

L5

1 Use compasses to construct triangles that have these length sides.

   a 9 cm, 4 cm, 7 cm
   b 7 cm, 5 cm, 6 cm

> Draw the longest side. Draw an arc at each end, with the radius set to the length of a shorter side. The arcs intersect at the third vertex of the triangle.

2 **a** Construct an equilateral triangle with sides of length 8 cm.
  b On your triangle construct the lines of symmetry.

3 Jonah swims across a swimming pool 12 m wide.
  His friend Wally is opposite him on the other side of the pool
  He swims across the pool diagonally and actually swims a
  distance of 16 m.

   a Make an accurate scale drawing showing the position of Jonah,
      Wally and the path that Jonah swam.
      Use a scale of 1 cm : 2 m.
   b Use your diagram to find the distance of Jonah from Wally after the swim.

L6

4 Construct two different isosceles triangles.
  Each triangle must have one side 5 cm and one side 8 cm long.

5 Construct a rhombus with sides of length 4 cm.

6 A triangle has an area of 15 cm².
  One side of the triangle is 5 cm.

   a If the triangle is a right-angled triangle, construct the triangle.
   b If the triangle is isosceles, construct the triangle.

L7

7 **a** Construct a right-angled triangle with shorter sides of length
      5 cm and 8 cm.
   b Measure the hypotenuse of your triangle.
   c Use Pythagoras' theorem to check the accuracy of your drawing and measuring.

8 The diagram shows two points P and Q.

  The locus of all points that are the same
  distance from P and Q is a straight line.
  Copy the diagram and construct this line.

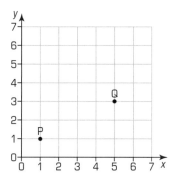

9 X and Y mark the positions of two villages, 10 km apart.

  A mobile phone mast is to be built less than 7 km from X.
  It is to be built closer to Y than it is to X.

  Copy the diagram and show the area where the mobile phone mast can be placed.

X•   •Y

Scale 1 cm : 1 km

▶ A shape has reflection symmetry if it folds onto itself.

▶ A shape has rotational symmetry if it turns onto itself more than once during a full turn.
The number of times it repeats is the order of rotational symmetry.

KEYWORDS
Reflection   Rotation
Translation   Enlargement
Scale factor   Centre
Mirror line

When you reflect, rotate or translate an object, the image is congruent.

▶ In a **reflection**, the object and its image are the same distance away from the mirror line.

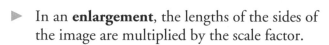

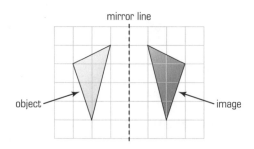

The mirror line is also called the axis of symmetry.

▶ In a **rotation**, an object is rotated about a centre point through an angle (anticlockwise is positive).

The blue triangle has been rotated through 90° anticlockwise with centre (1, 2).

Use tracing paper to rotate a shape.
Keep the centre point in place with the point of a pencil.

▶ In a **translation**, every point of an object moves the same distance and direction.

The blue triangle has been translated through $\begin{pmatrix} 4 \\ 3 \end{pmatrix}$.

This is 4 units to the right and 3 units up.

A translation $\begin{pmatrix} -5 \\ -2 \end{pmatrix}$ means 5 units to the left and 2 units down.

▶ In an **enlargement**, the lengths of the sides of the image are multiplied by the scale factor.

▶ The distance of the image from the centre of enlargement is the scale factor times the distance of the object from the centre of enlargement.

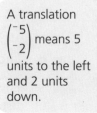

▶ The image is a different size, but the same shape.

A scale factor of $\frac{1}{2}$ means that the lengths of the image are half those of the object.

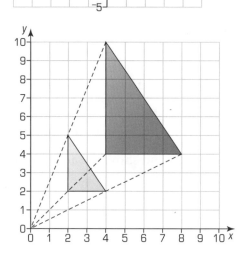

The blue triangle has been enlarged with scale factor 2 with centre of enlargement (0, 0).

You join corresponding vertices to find the centre of enlargement.

Exercise S7

L5

1 Jonie has these four identical squares.

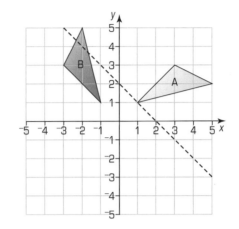

Show how they can fit together to make a pattern with:

a 4 lines of symmetry
b no lines of symmetry
c rotational symmetry of order 2.

2 The diagram shows two triangles A and B.

a Triangle A is rotated onto triangle B.
What is the centre of rotation?
What is the angle of rotation?

b Copy the diagram and reflect triangle A
in the mirror line.
Label the image triangle C.
Write down the coordinates of the vertices
of triangle C.

L6

3 On a copy of the grid, draw an enlargement of the
arrowhead with scale factor 2.
Use point C as the centre of enlargement.

4 On the diagram, the large T-shape is an
enlargement of the smaller T-shape.
What is the scale factor of the
enlargement?
Write down the coordinates of the centre
of enlargement.

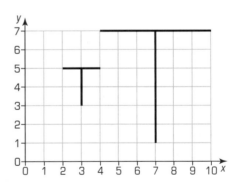

L7

5 A picture of a cat measures 8 cm wide by 4.5 cm high.

a The picture is to be enlarged so that it just fits inside a rectangle
that measures 18 cm wide by 9 cm.
By what scale factor should the original picture be enlarged?

b The picture is used so that it just fits onto a badge.
The badge is 3 cm by 1.5 cm.
By what scale factor was the original picture multiplied?

6 Two rectangles are drawn to that one is an enlargement of the other.
The smaller rectangle has side lengths of 3 cm and 5 cm.
One side of the larger rectangle is 30 cm.
What are the possible scale factors of the enlargement?

▶ Metric measures are based on powers of 10.

1 km = 1000 m
1 m = 100 cm
1 cm = 10 mm
1 kg = 1000 g
1 litre = 1000 ml

1 ml of water weighs 1 g and fills 1 mm³.

You need to have an idea of the size of different lengths.

| 1 km is $2\frac{1}{2}$ times round a track. | 1 m is the width of a door. | 1 cm is about the width of a fingernail. | 1 mm is about the width of a blade of grass. |

Measures can be given in metric or imperial units.
You need to be able to convert between them:

Length	Weight	Capacity
1 inch ≈ 2.5 cm	1 ounce ≈ 28 g	1 pint ≈ 0.6 litre
1 foot ≈ 30 cm	1 pound ≈ 450 g	1 litre ≈ 0.22 gallon
1 yard ≈ 90 cm	1 kg ≈ 2.2 pounds	1 gallon ≈ 4.5 litres
5 miles ≈ 8 km		

You need to know the relationship between speed, distance and time.

example
Change these amounts into metric units:
a 6 ounces   **b** 40 pounds   **c** 12.5 miles
....
a $6 \times 28 = 168$ g   **b** $40 \div 2.2 = 18$ kg   **c** $12.5 \times \frac{8}{5} = 20$ km

In all conversions think carefully whether you need to multiply or divide.

$$\text{Speed} = \frac{\text{distance}}{\text{time}} \qquad \text{Time} = \frac{\text{distance}}{\text{speed}}$$

Distance = speed × time

This triangle can help:

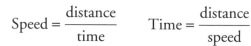

example
It takes me 45 minutes to walk 3 miles home from school.
What is my average speed in miles per hour?
....
You need the time in hours and distance in miles.
45 minutes = $\frac{3}{4}$ hour
Average speed = distance ÷ time = $3 \div \frac{3}{4} = 4$ mph

Remember to give the units in your answers.

Exercise S8

L5

1 A water bottle holds 500 ml.
An adult needs 1.8 litres of water to drink each day.

   a How many water bottles are needed for one day? 4
   b Jon goes on a three-day trek and takes all his water with him.
      What is the minimum number of water bottles that Jon needs to
      take on the trek? 5 and

2 A ruler is marked in inches and centimetres.

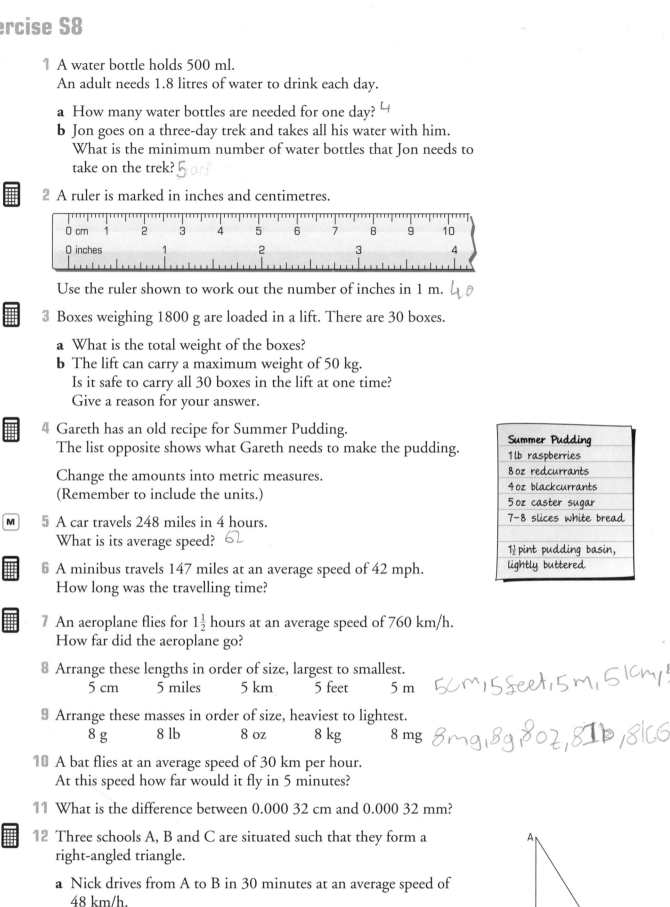

   Use the ruler shown to work out the number of inches in 1 m. 40

3 Boxes weighing 1800 g are loaded in a lift. There are 30 boxes.

   a What is the total weight of the boxes?
   b The lift can carry a maximum weight of 50 kg.
      Is it safe to carry all 30 boxes in the lift at one time?
      Give a reason for your answer.

4 Gareth has an old recipe for Summer Pudding.
The list opposite shows what Gareth needs to make the pudding.

   Change the amounts into metric measures.
   (Remember to include the units.)

Summer Pudding
1 lb raspberries
8 oz redcurrants
4 oz blackcurrants
5 oz caster sugar
7–8 slices white bread

1½ pint pudding basin,
lightly buttered

L6 **M**

5 A car travels 248 miles in 4 hours.
What is its average speed? 62

6 A minibus travels 147 miles at an average speed of 42 mph.
How long was the travelling time?

7 An aeroplane flies for $1\frac{1}{2}$ hours at an average speed of 760 km/h.
How far did the aeroplane go?

8 Arrange these lengths in order of size, largest to smallest.
    5 cm   5 miles   5 km   5 feet   5 m   5km,5feet,5m,5km,5miles

9 Arrange these masses in order of size, heaviest to lightest.
    8 g   8 lb   8 oz   8 kg   8 mg   8mg,8g,8oz,8lb,8kg

L7

10 A bat flies at an average speed of 30 km per hour.
At this speed how far would it fly in 5 minutes?

11 What is the difference between 0.000 32 cm and 0.000 32 mm?

12 Three schools A, B and C are situated such that they form a
right-angled triangle.

   a Nick drives from A to B in 30 minutes at an average speed of
      48 km/h.
      How far is school A from school B?
   b Nick then drives from B to C at the same average speed.
      B is 7 km from C.
      How long does it take for Nick to drive from B to C?
   c How far is school A from school C?
   d Nick drives from school C to school A in 30 minutes.
      What was his average speed for this journey?

Compound area and perimeter

▶ The perimeter, P, is the total distance around a flat shape.

▶ The area, A, is the amount of space covered by a flat shape.

KEYWORDS
Triangle   Rectangle
Parallelogram   Trapezium

To calculate area and perimeter all dimensions must be in the same units.

You should know how to find the area of these shapes.

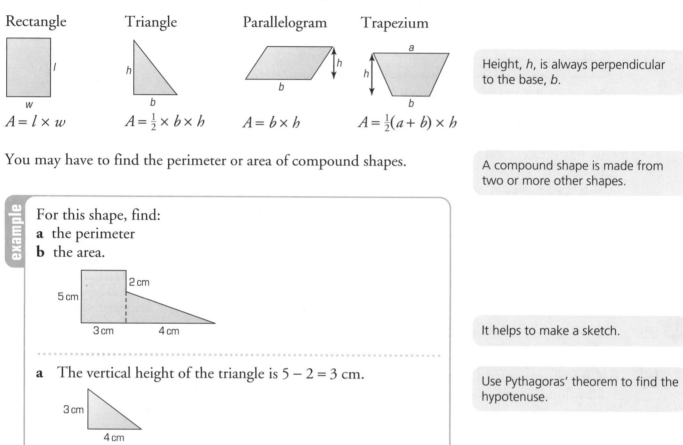

Rectangle   Triangle   Parallelogram   Trapezium

$A = l \times w$ $A = \frac{1}{2} \times b \times h$ $A = b \times h$ $A = \frac{1}{2}(a + b) \times h$

Height, h, is always perpendicular to the base, b.

You may have to find the perimeter or area of compound shapes.

A compound shape is made from two or more other shapes.

---

example

For this shape, find:
a the perimeter
b the area.

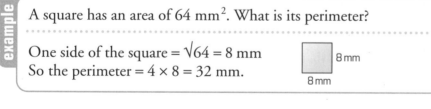

It helps to make a sketch.

. . . .

a The vertical height of the triangle is $5 - 2 = 3$ cm.

Use Pythagoras' theorem to find the hypotenuse.

The hypotenuse $= \sqrt{3^2 + 4^2} = 5$ cm
So the perimeter of the shape $= 4 + 3 + 5 + 3 + 2 + 5 = 22$ cm

b Area of rectangle $= 5 \times 3 = 15$
Area of triangle $= \frac{1}{2} \times 4 \times 3 = 6$
So the total area $= 15 + 6 = 21$ cm^2

---

example

A square has an area of 64 mm^2. What is its perimeter?

. . . .

One side of the square $= \sqrt{64} = 8$ mm
So the perimeter $= 4 \times 8 = 32$ mm.

8 mm

8 mm

---

example

One side of a rectangle is n cm long.
The other side of the rectangle is 4 cm long.
Write expressions for the: **a** area   **b** perimeter.

. . . .

a $A = 4 \times n$ or $A = 4n$
b $P = 2 \times (n + 4) = 2n + 8$

4 cm

n cm

Exercise S9

L5 **M** **1** A square has an area of 49 cm².
What is its perimeter?

2 **a** A square has a perimeter of 20 cm.
What is the area of the square?
b Write down the sizes of all the rectangles that have a perimeter
of 20 cm where the sides have integer (whole number) values.
Work out the area of each rectangle.
c Look at your answers to parts **a** and **b**.
What is special about the rectangle with the largest area?

3 A rectangle has a perimeter of 12 cm.
The length is twice the width.
Find the area of this rectangle.

L6 **4** The box describes three squares.
Put X, Y and Z in order of size from smallest to largest.
Show calculations to explain how you worked out your
answer.

> X, Y and Z are all squares.
> X has a perimeter of 24 cm.
> Y has an area of 24 cm².
> Z has one side with length 24 cm.

5 Each shape below has an area of 48 cm².
Find the height of each shape.

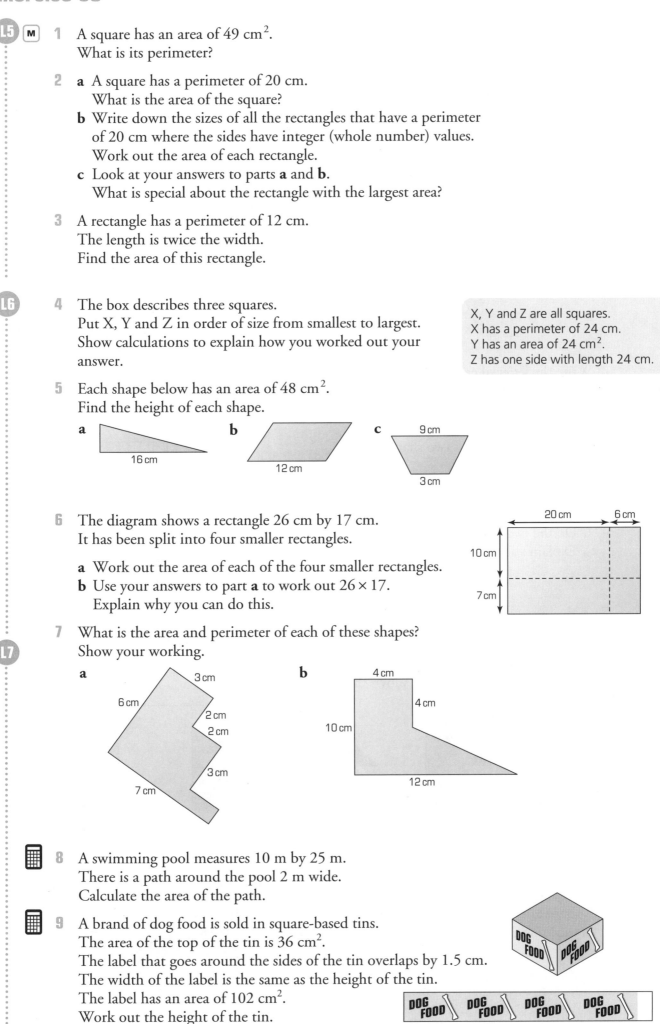

a 16 cm
b 12 cm
c 9 cm 3 cm

6 The diagram shows a rectangle 26 cm by 17 cm.
It has been split into four smaller rectangles.

a Work out the area of each of the four smaller rectangles.
b Use your answers to part **a** to work out 26 × 17.
Explain why you can do this.

20 cm   6 cm
10 cm
7 cm

L7 **7** What is the area and perimeter of each of these shapes?
Show your working.

a 3 cm
6 cm
2 cm
2 cm
3 cm
7 cm

b 4 cm
4 cm
10 cm
12 cm

8 A swimming pool measures 10 m by 25 m.
There is a path around the pool 2 m wide.
Calculate the area of the path.

9 A brand of dog food is sold in square-based tins.
The area of the top of the tin is 36 cm².
The label that goes around the sides of the tin overlaps by 1.5 cm.
The width of the label is the same as the height of the tin.
The label has an area of 102 cm².
Work out the height of the tin.

L5

1 An equilateral triangle has
3 lines of symmetry.

It has **rotational symmetry of order 3**.

(S7)

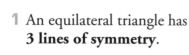

Here are six shapes labelled A to F.

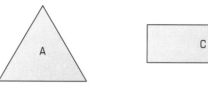

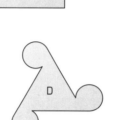

Write the letter of each shape in the correct space in a copy of the table.
You may use a mirror or tracing paper to help you.
The letters for the first two shapes have been written for you.

		number of lines of symmetry			
		0	1	2	3
order of rotational symmetry	1				
	2	B			
	3				A

2 a I have a square piece of card.
I cut along the dashed line to make two pieces of card.
Do the two pieces of card have the **same area**?
Explain your answer.

(S9)

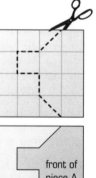

b The card is shaded **blue** on the front, and **black** on the back.
I turn piece A over to see its black side.
Which of the shapes below shows the black side of piece A?

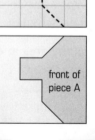

front of piece A

P   Q   R   S   T

L6

3 Four cubes join to make an L-shape.
The diagram shows the L-shape after **quarter turns** in one direction.
On a copy of the grid, draw the L-shape after the **next** quarter turn in the same direction.

(S4)

L6

4 Jenny and Alan each have a rectangle made out of paper.
One side is 10 cm.
The other side is n cm.

S9

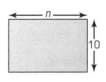

a They write expressions for the **perimeter** of the rectangle.

Jenny writes   2n + 20
Alan writes   2(n + 10)

Which of these statements is correct?
A Jenny is correct and Alan is wrong.   **B** Jenny is wrong and Alan is correct.
C Both Jenny and Alan are correct.   **D** Both Jenny and Alan are wrong.

b Alan cuts his rectangle, then puts the two halves side by side.

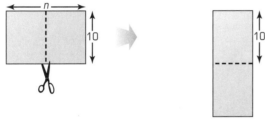

Alan's new rectangle

What is the perimeter of Alan's new rectangle?
Write your expression as simply as possible.

c Jenny cuts her rectangle a different way, and puts one half
below the other.

Jenny's new rectangle

What is the perimeter of Jenny's new rectangle?
Write your expression as simply as possible.

d What value of n would make the perimeter of Jenny's new
rectangle the **same value** as the perimeter of Alan's new rectangle?

L7

5 A gardener wants to plant a tree.
She wants it to be **more than 8 m** away from the **vegetable plot**.
She wants it to be **more than 12 m** away from the **greenhouse**.
The plan below shows part of the garden.
The scale is **1 cm** to **4 m**.

S6

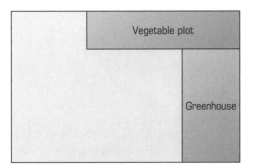

Trace the diagram.
Show **accurately** on the plan the region of the garden where she can plant the tree.
Label this region **R**.

▶ A **circle** is a set of points equidistant from a centre point.

▶ The **circumference**, *C*, is the distance around the circle.

▶ The **radius**, *r*, is the distance from the centre to the circumference.

▶ The **diameter**, *d*, is distance across the circle through the centre.

An **arc** is part of the circumference.
A **sector** is a region bounded by an arc and two radii.

A **chord** joins two points on the circumference.
It divides a circle into two **segments**.

KEYWORDS

Arc	Chord
Sector	Segment
Radius	Diameter
Circumference	

You can use these formulae to calculate the circumference and area of a circle:

▶ Circumference, $C = 2 \times \pi \times r$ or $\pi \times d$

▶ Area, $A = \pi \times r^2$

Use $\pi = 3$ for estimates and mental calculations.

Use the π button on your calculator or use $\pi = \frac{22}{7}$ or $\pi = 3.142$.

> **example**
>
> Find the circumference and area of a circle with radius 5 cm.
>
> Substitute $r = 5$ into $C = 2 \times \pi \times r$:
> $C = 2 \times \pi \times 5 = 31.4$ cm (to 1 dp)
>
> Substitute $r = 5$ into $A = \pi \times r^2$:
> $A = \pi \times 5^2 = 78.5$ cm^2 (to 1 dp)

You can solve circle problems using the formulae.

> **example**
>
> Jamie uses a trundle wheel to measure the length of the school playground.
> The diameter of the wheel is 45 cm.
>
> **a** What does one turn of the trundle wheel measure?
> **b** The length of the playground is 72.3 metres.
>   How many complete turns did Jamie's wheel make?
>
> ⋯⋯⋯⋯⋯⋯⋯⋯⋯⋯⋯⋯⋯⋯⋯⋯⋯⋯⋯⋯⋯⋯⋯
>
> **a** The diameter is 45 cm so the circumference is $\pi \times d$.
> $C = 3.14 \times 45 = 141.3$ cm (to 1 dp)
> **b** 141.3 cm is 1.413 m so one turn is 1.413 m.
>   72.3 m ÷ 1.143 m = 63.25 (to 2 dp)
>   The wheel made 63 complete turns.

It helps to draw a sketch:

45 cm

Remember to give the accuracy of answer required in the question.

Exercise S10

1 What is the approximate circumference of a circle with diameter 4 cm?

2 What is the approximate area of a circle with radius 6 cm?

3 Explain why the largest chord in a circle is the diameter.

4 A trundle wheel is used to measure distance.
A trundle wheel measures 100 cm with each complete rotation.
What is the diameter of the wheel?

5 Class 9C make a trundle wheel with radius 30 cm.

  a What is the circumference of this trundle wheel?
  b Class 9C use the wheel to measure the length of the school car park.
  The wheel makes 64 rotations.
  Calculate the length, to the nearest metre, of the school car park.

6 Jason and Rachel each build a go-cart.

The wheels of Jason's go-cart have diameter 90 cm.
  a Jason pushes the wheel round exactly once.
  Calculate how far the go-cart has moved.

The wheels of Rachel's go-cart have diameter 45 cm.
  b How many times would Rachel need to push the wheels on her
  go-cart round so that she travels the same distance as Jason?

7 A circle has a radius of 12 cm. Calculate the area of the circle.

8 A circle has a circumference of 120 cm. Calculate the radius of the circle.

9 The area, in square centimetres, of a circle is 16π.
What is the radius of the circle?

10 A tin of beans has diameter 6 cm and height
8 cm.
The label that wraps around the tin is removed
and laid flat.
Calculate the area of the label.

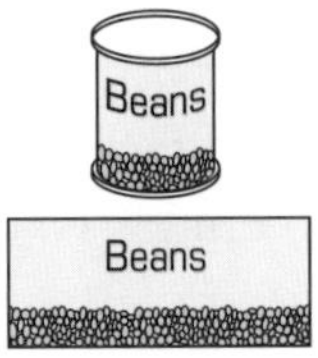

11 A circle is drawn inside a square.
The circle touches the edges of the square.
The square has sides of length 10 cm.
What fraction of the square does the circle cover?
Show all your working.

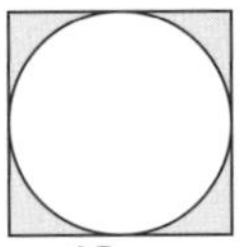

12 A round table has diameter 120 cm.
To sit comfortably at the table a person needs 45 cm around the circumference.
How many people can sit comfortably around this table?

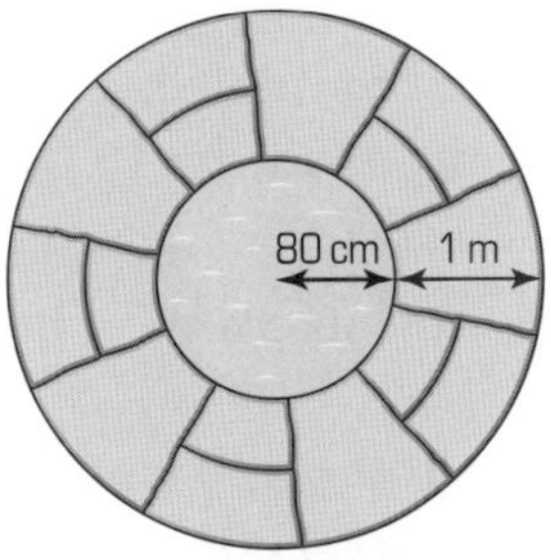

13 A circular pond of radius 80 cm is dug in a garden.
There is a path around the pond 1 m wide.
What is the area of the path?

14 The diagram shows two circles with radii 2 cm and 7 cm.
The smaller circle lies completely inside the larger circle.

Work out the blue area.

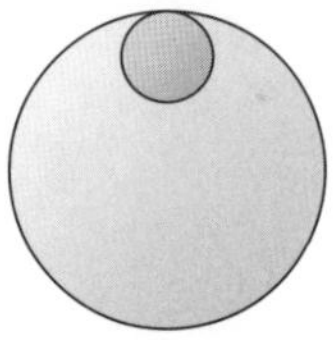

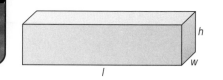
▶ The **surface area** is the total area of all the surfaces of a shape.

To calculate the surface area you must have all dimensions in the same units.

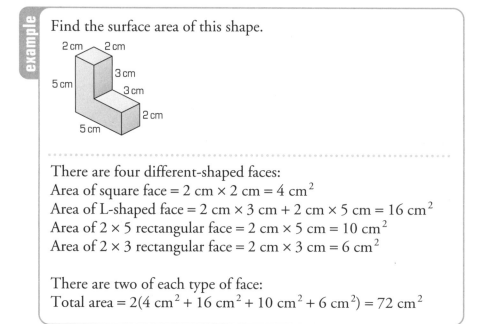

KEYWORDS
Surface area   Prism
Cuboid

Surface area of a cuboid = $2(l \times w) + 2(w \times h) + 2(h \times l)$

To find the surface area of shapes like prisms, find the area of each surface then add them.

A prism has a constant cross-section.

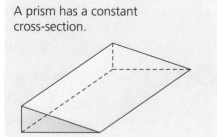

example

Find the surface area of this shape.

2 cm   2 cm
3 cm
5 cm
3 cm
2 cm
5 cm

There are four different-shaped faces:
Area of square face = $2 \text{ cm} \times 2 \text{ cm} = 4 \text{ cm}^2$
Area of L-shaped face = $2 \text{ cm} \times 3 \text{ cm} + 2 \text{ cm} \times 5 \text{ cm} = 16 \text{ cm}^2$
Area of 2×5 rectangular face = $2 \text{ cm} \times 5 \text{ cm} = 10 \text{ cm}^2$
Area of 2×3 rectangular face = $2 \text{ cm} \times 3 \text{ cm} = 6 \text{ cm}^2$

There are two of each type of face:
Total area = $2(4 \text{ cm}^2 + 16 \text{ cm}^2 + 10 \text{ cm}^2 + 6 \text{ cm}^2) = 72 \text{ cm}^2$

▶ The metric units of area are mm^2, cm^2, m^2 and km^2.

You can fit $10 \text{ mm} \times 10 \text{ mm} = 100 \text{ mm}^2$ inside a $1 \text{ cm} \times 1 \text{ cm}$ square.

▶ To change cm^2 to mm^2 multiply by 100.
▶ To change mm^2 to cm^2 divide by 100.

1 cm = 10 mm

You can fit $100 \text{ cm} \times 100 \text{ cm} = 10\,000 \text{ cm}^2$ inside a $1 \text{ m} \times 1 \text{ m}$ square.

▶ To change m^2 to cm^2 multiply by 10 000.
▶ To change cm^2 to m^2 divide by 10 000.

1 m = 100 cm

example

Write **a** $42\,000 \text{ mm}^2$ in cm^2 **b** 6.3 m^2 in cm^2.

a $42\,000 \text{ mm}^2 \div 100 = 420 \text{ cm}^2$
b $6.3 \text{ m}^2 \times 10\,000 = 63\,000 \text{ cm}^2$

Exercise S11

L5

1 Two cuboids are made by joining together six cubes as shown in the diagrams.

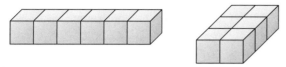

Calculate the surface area of each cuboid.

L6

2 The diagram shows the net for a cuboid.
Calculate the surface area of the cuboid.
Assume each square is 1 cm².

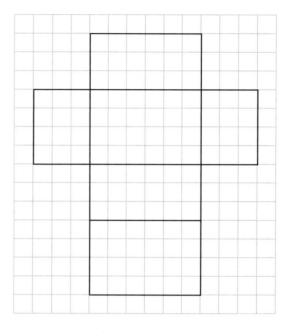

3 A box of chocolates is made in the shape of a triangular prism.
Calculate the surface area of the box.

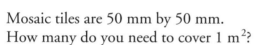

4 Mosaic tiles are 50 mm by 50 mm.
How many do you need to cover 1 m²?

M **5** The surface area of a cuboid is 560 000 cm².
What is the surface area of the cuboid in **a** m² **b** mm²?

L7 **M** **6** A cube has surface area 60 000 cm².
Write down the length of one side of the cube.

7 Calculate the surface area of a cylinder of radius 4 cm and height 9 cm.

8 Calculate the surface area of this wedge.
Give your answer to the nearest whole number.

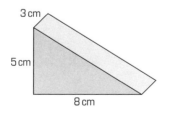

9 The surface area of a cuboid 40 cm².
The cuboid has a pair of squares faces.
The edges of the cuboid are all whole number values in cm.
If one edge of the cuboid is 2 cm, what are the lengths of the other two edges?

▶ **Volume** is the amount of space taken up by an object.

To calculate volume you must have all dimensions in the same units.

KEYWORDS
Volume   Cylinder
Cuboid   Prism

▶ Volume of a cuboid = $l \times w \times h$

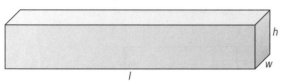

▶ Volume of a prism = $A \times l$

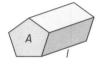

A is the area of the cross-section.

---

example

Find the volume of this cylinder.

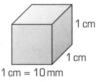
3.6 cm
8.2 cm

Always round your answer to a sensible number.

Area of circle = $A = \pi \times 3.6^2$
Volume = $\pi \times 3.6^2 \times 8.2 = 333.9$ cm^3

You can fit 10 mm × 10 mm × 10 mm = 1000 mm^3 inside a 1 cm × 1 cm × 1 cm cube.

▶ To change cm^3 to mm^3 multiply by 1000.

▶ To change mm^3 to cm^3 divide by 1000.

1 cm
1 cm
1 cm = 10 mm

You can fit 100 cm × 100 cm × 100 cm = 1 000 000 cm^3 inside a 1 m × 1 m × 1 m cube.

▶ To change m^3 to cm^3 multiply by 1 000 000.

▶ To change cm^3 to m^3 divide by 1 000 000.

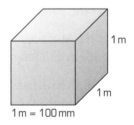
1 m
1 m
1 m = 100 mm

---

example

Cuboid A has length 6 cm, width 4 cm and height 15 cm.
Cuboid B has length 90 mm, width 50 mm and height 80 mm.
Show that the cuboids have the same volume.

Volume of A = $6 \times 4 \times 15 = 360$ cm^3
Volume of B = $90 \times 50 \times 80$
$= 360\,000$ mm^3
$= 360\,000 \div 1000$ cm^3
$= 360$ cm^3

Exercise S12

L5

1 Two cuboids are made by joining together six cubes as shown in the diagrams.

Calculate the volume of each cuboid.

L6

2 The diagram shows the net for a cuboid.
The net is folded up to make a cuboid.
Calculate the volume of the cuboid.

3 A box of chocolates is made in
the shape of a triangular prism.
Calculate the volume of the
box.

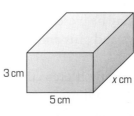

5 cm
3 cm
7 cm
4 cm

4 What is the volume of a cuboid measuring 3 cm by 5 cm by 8 cm?

[M] **5** A cube has volume 27 cm^3. What is the side length of the cube?

[M] **6** A shape has volume 0.04 m^3. What is its volume in   **a** cm^3 **b** mm^3?

7 A seed bed measures 2 m long, 60 cm wide and 20 cm deep.
How much earth will it hold?

8 These two cuboids have the same volume.

A

4 cm
6 cm
5 cm

B

3 cm
x cm
5 cm

  a What is the volume of cuboid A?   **b** Work out the length marked x.

L7

9 Calculate the volume of a cylinder of radius
4 cm and height 9 cm.

4 cm
9 cm

10 Calculate the volume of this wedge.
Give your answer to the nearest whole number.

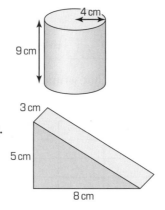

3 cm
5 cm
8 cm

A set of data is made up of pieces of information.

▶ **Primary data** is data that you collect yourself.

▶ **Secondary data** is data that has already been collected.

You can carry out a survey or experiment to collect data.

▶ You need a data collection sheet to record the data you collect.

▶ You need to choose a sample that will not be biased.

A questionnaire is a list of questions used to gather data in a survey.

▶ Use answer boxes that cover all possible answers and do not overlap.

> **KEYWORDS**
> Questionnaire   Data
> Secondary   Primary
> Survey   Sample
> Experiment   Bias

example

Ellie carried out a survey to find out how much money students spend in the school canteen each week and what they buy.

Ellie asked 20 of her friends.

a Explain why this might not give very good data.

b One of Ellie's questions was:

> How much do you usually spend on drinks each week?
> ☐ A lot ☐ A little ☐ Nothing ☐ Don't know

Explain what is wrong with the choices she has given and write new labels for the boxes.

Ellie sorted what people bought into three categories: lunch, snacks and drinks.
No one spent more than £15 in a week.

c Design a data collection sheet for Ellie to collect the data.

· ·

a Ellie's friends may all buy the same type of food and may all be girls. This data may be biased.
Ellie should ask boys and girls and students from each school year.

b 'A lot' and 'a little' mean different things to different people so you should specify amounts.
Make sure that the amounts do not overlap and that there are no gaps so that students can tick only one box.
For example:

> ☐ Nothing ☐ Less than £5 ☐ £5–10 ☐ Over £10

c This is a two-way table that would be straightforward for Ellie to use:

	Nothing	Less than £5	£5–£10	Over £10
Lunch				
Snacks				
Drinks				

Exercise D1

L5

1 A new chocolate bar is being developed.
It is given to schoolchildren to test in a survey.

    a **i** Is the data being collected primary data or secondary data?
       ii Give one disadvantage of asking only schoolchildren.
      iii Give one advantage of asking only schoolchildren.

The people who took part in the survey had to answer this question:

Did you like the chocolate bar?	☐ Yes	☐ A lot	☐ A little	☐ No

b Mo said the labels on the two middle boxes need changing.
Explain why Mo is right.

They were also asked:

How much would you pay for the bar?	☐ Under 40p	☐ Over 40p	☐ Up to 60p

c Mo said some boxes on this question also need changing.
Write new labels for as many boxes as you think need changing.
d Design a two-way table to collect responses to both these questions.

2 Some students plan a survey to find out what type of holiday people prefer.

Design 1	**Design 2**	**Design 3**
Write down the type of holiday people prefer. For example: Camping, hotel, self-catering …	Use a tally chart to record the holiday preferred. For example:	Use a code to record the preferred type of holiday. For example: Camping – C Hotel – H Youth hostel – Y …

Design 2 table:

Holiday	Tally	Frequency
Camping		
Hotel		
Self-catering		

The students will only use one design.
a Choose a design that they should not use.
Explain why the students should not use it.
b Choose the best design to use.
Explain why the students should use this diagram.

L6

3 A local council said in its annual report:

> '68% of households recycle their plastic, glass and paper each week.'

Lexie thought that more than 68% of households recycled plastic, glass and paper.
She decided to do a survey and asked 20 people who lived in her street.
Give two different reasons why Lexie's sample might not give very good data.

4 Children in Crayton begin school in:
  ▷ September if their birthday is from September to February
  ▷ January if their birthday is from March to August.
Jenny wants to investigate if more children who start school earlier,
in September, are in the top maths set.
She decides to ask 16 of her friends in her year group what maths set they are in.
Give two different ways in which Jenny could improve her survey.

An average is a representative value of a set of data.

▶ The **mode** is the value that occurs most often.
There can be more than one mode in a data set.
▶ The **median** is the middle value when the data is arranged in order.
▶ The **mean** is calculated by adding all the values then dividing by the number of pieces of data.

The range represents the spread of the data.

▶ Range = largest value − smallest value

example

Tom has 4 number cards:
The mean of these cards is 7.

| 6 | 8 | 9 | 5 |

Tom has a fifth card. What could the number be if:

a the mean stays the same   **b** the mode is 8
c the median is 6   **d** the range stays the same?

....

a Total of 5 cards = 5 × 7 = 35
Fifth card = Total of 5 cards − Total of 4 cards = 35 − 28 = 7
b There is currently no mode, so an extra 8 will give a mode of 8.
c Put the 4 cards in order: 5, 6, 8, 9
A number of 6 or less will make the median 6.
d The lowest and highest values must stay the same.
The card can be 5, 6, 7, 8 or 9.

For a large set of data,
$$\text{median} = \frac{(n + 1)^{th}}{2} \text{ value}$$

You can use an **assumed mean** to calculate the mean of large values:

▶ Assume a convenient value for the mean.
▶ Subtract it from each piece of data.
▶ Find the mean of the differences.
▶ Mean = assumed mean + mean of differences

Check your answer is sensible – it must be within the range of values.

example

The table shows the contents of 30 matchboxes. Find the mean number of matches per box.

Number of matches	32	33	34	35	36
Frequency	4	6	12	5	3

....

Assume a mean of 30. Subtract 30 from each number of matches: 2, 3, 4, 5, 6
Mean of differences = ((2 × 4) + (3 × 6) + (4 × 12) + (5 × 5) + (6 × 3)) ÷ 30 = 3.9
Mean number of matches = assumed mean + mean of differences = 30 + 3.9 = 33.9

A **stem-and-leaf diagram** shows the shape of a distribution.

A stem-and-leaf diagram needs a key.

example

The stem-and-leaf diagram shows the speed of cars travelling up a hill.

Find: **a** the range   **b** the median.

....

a Range = 62 − 28 = 34
b Median = $\frac{(15 + 1)}{2}$th value = 50 mph

```
6 | 2
5 | 0 1 4 6 7 8 8
4 | 2 5 7 9
3 | 3 6
2 | 8
Key: 4 | 2  means 42 mph
```

This is the stem.

These are leaves.
They are in order.

Exercise D2

L5

1 The mean of these four numbers is 8.

    5   6   9   12

Write four numbers with a mean of 9.

2 The median of these seven numbers is 10.

    5   6   8   10   11   12   12

Write a set of six numbers with a median of 10.

3 There are three children in Jo's family.
The range of their shoe sizes is 2.
Two of them wear size 7 shoes.
What are the possible shoe sizes of the other child in Jo's family?

4 Write down two numbers that have a mean of 7 and a range of 3.

L6 **M**

5 Work out the number that is halfway between 8×29 and 12×29.

6 Four number cards are placed face down on a table so that their numbers are hidden.
The mode of the numbers is 6.
The mean of the numbers is 5.
What are the numbers on each of the four number cards?

7 Robbie has three number cards.
The numbers on the cards are all hidden.
The mode of the numbers on the cards is 4.
The mean of the numbers is 5.
What are the numbers on the cards?

8 Terry has three number cards.
The mean of these three numbers is 6.
Terry chooses another card.

| 3 | 7 | 8 |

  a If the mean is still 6, what is the number on the card?
  b If the mean goes down by 1, what is the number on the card?

L7

9 The stem-and-leaf diagram shows the heights, in cm, of a sample of Year 9 girls.

```
17| 0 1              Key:
16| 2 4 5 7 7 9      16 | 2  means 162 cm
15| 0 0 2 2 3 4 6 8 8
14| 7 8
```

Find for this data: **a** the median   **b** the range.

M **10** The mean of two numbers is 5.
One of the numbers is ⁻3. What is the other number?

11 The table shows the number of tries scored by a rugby team in 16 matches one season.

Number of tries scored	0	1	2	3	4
Number of matches	1	3	4	7	1

  a Show that the total number of tries scored is 36.
  b Calculate the mean number of tries per match.

12 The table shows the shoe sizes of a group of 24 girls.

Shoe size	3	$3\frac{1}{2}$	4	$4\frac{1}{2}$	5	$5\frac{1}{2}$	6	$6\frac{1}{2}$	4
Frequency	1	0	3	0	7	4	4	2	3

  a Write down the modal shoe size of this group of girls.
  b Calculate the mean shoe size of this group of girls.
  c Which of these two averages is the best one to use?
     Give a reason for your choice.

L5

1 Some pupils wanted to find out if people liked a new biscuit.
They decided to do a survey and wrote a questionnaire.

  a One question was:

    How old are you (in years)?

    ☐   ☐   ☐   ☐   ☐

    20 or younger   20 to 30   30 to 40   40 to 50   50 or older

    Mary said: 'The labels for the middle three boxes need changing.'
    Explain why Mary was **right**.

  b A different question was:

    How much do you usually spend on biscuits each week?

    ☐ a lot   ☐ a little   ☐ nothing   ☐ don't know

    Mary said: 'Some of these labels need changing too'.
    Write new labels for any boxes that need changing.
    You may change as many labels as you want to.

The pupils decide to give their questionnaire to 50 people.
Jon said: 'Let's ask 50 pupils in our school.'

  c Give **one disadvantage** of Jon's suggestion.

  d Give **one advantage** of Jon's suggestion.

L6

2 The diagram shows a circle and a square.

  a The radius of the circle is 12 mm.
    What is the **area** of the circle to the
    nearest mm^2?
    Show your working.

12 mm   Not drawn accurately

  b The **ratio** of the area of the **circle** to the area of the **square** is **2 : 1**
    What is the area of the square to the nearest mm^2?

  c What is the side length of the square?
    Show your working.

3 The squared paper shows the nets of cuboid A and cuboid B.

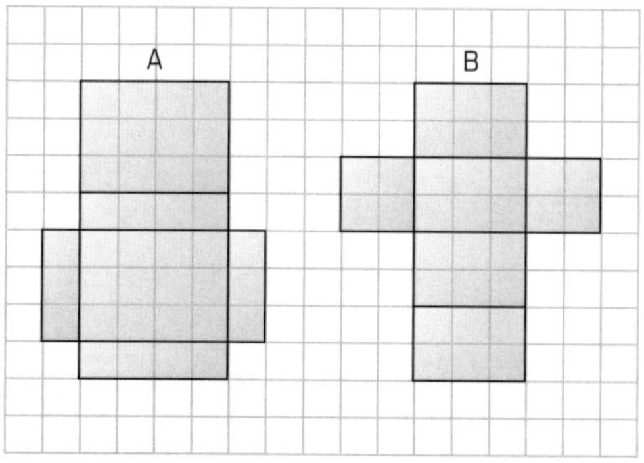

  a Do the cuboids have the **same surface area**?
    Show calculations to explain how you know.

  b Do the cuboids have the **same volume**?
    Show calculations to explain how you know.

L6 🖩 **4** **a** What is the volume of this **standard size** box of salt? ⓢ12

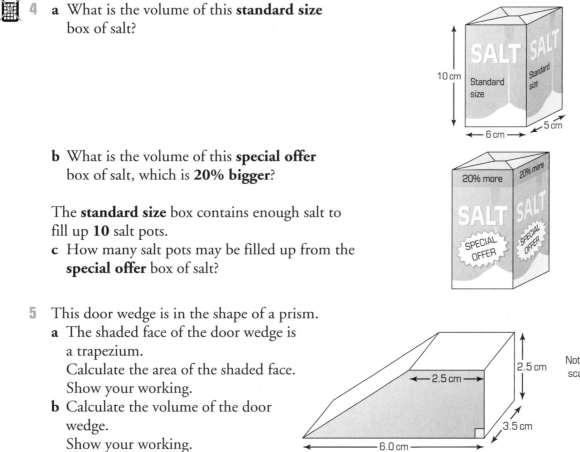

SALT SALT
Standard size   Standard size
10 cm
← 6 cm → ↙ 5 cm

b What is the volume of this **special offer** box of salt, which is **20% bigger**?

20% more   20% more
SALT SALT
SPECIAL OFFER   SPECIAL OFFER

The **standard size** box contains enough salt to fill up **10** salt pots.
c How many salt pots may be filled up from the **special offer** box of salt?

5 This door wedge is in the shape of a prism. ⓢ12
a The shaded face of the door wedge is a trapezium.
Calculate the area of the shaded face.
Show your working.
b Calculate the volume of the door wedge.
Show your working.

← 2.5 cm →
2.5 cm   Not to scale
3.5 cm
← 6.0 cm →

L7 **6** As part of a biology project, Dan and Ama are counting the number of peas in a sample of pea pods. These are their results for the first 50 pods. Dan and Ama correctly worked out the mode as 5 and the median as 6. Ⓓ2

Number of peas in a pod	Number of pods
3	2
4	7
5	14
6	12
7	10
8	5

a Work out the mean number of peas in a pod in their sample.
Show your working.
b Work out the number of peas in 200 pods.
You should first decide whether to use the mode, median or mean.
Show your working.
c About how many pods out of 200 would you expect to have 3 or 4 peas?
d Dan takes another pod at random from the sample, opens it, and counts the number of peas.
Work out the probability that the pod contains **more** than six peas.

► A **bar chart** or frequency diagram uses rectangles of equal width to display discrete data.
The frequency is given by the height of the rectangles.

► A multiple bar chart is a bar chart with two or more sets of bars. It is used to compare two or more data sets.

► A percentage bar chart shows the total frequency in a single bar. The bar is split into percentages in different categories.

Discrete data is countable.

---

example

The graph shows the different ways teachers travel to work at two schools, X and Y.

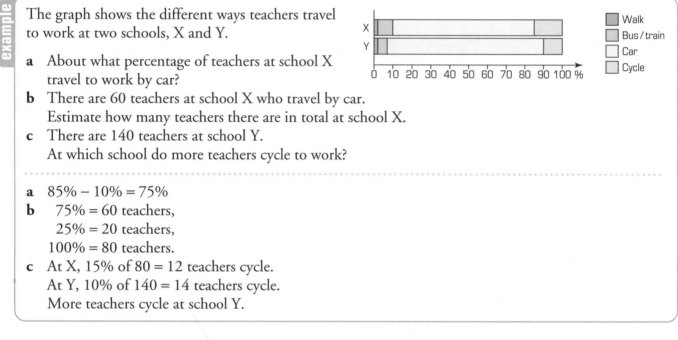

a About what percentage of teachers at school X travel to work by car?

b There are 60 teachers at school X who travel by car. Estimate how many teachers there are in total at school X.

c There are 140 teachers at school Y. At which school do more teachers cycle to work?

....

a $85\% - 10\% = 75\%$

b $75\% = 60$ teachers,
    $25\% = 20$ teachers,
    $100\% = 80$ teachers.

c At X, 15% of 80 = 12 teachers cycle.
   At Y, 10% of 140 = 14 teachers cycle.
   More teachers cycle at school Y.

► A frequency diagram is used to display continuous data.
The frequency is given by the height of the rectangles.
There are no gaps between the rectangles.

Continuous data is measurable.

---

example

The graph shows the waiting times of 50 customers at a supermarket checkout.

Estimate the probability that a customer will have to wait less than 3 minutes.

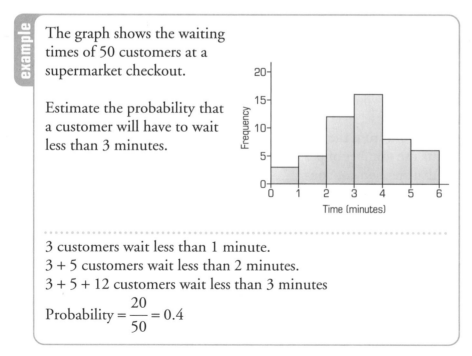

....

3 customers wait less than 1 minute.
3 + 5 customers wait less than 2 minutes.
3 + 5 + 12 customers wait less than 3 minutes

Probability $= \dfrac{20}{50} = 0.4$

See D7 for probability.

Exercise D3

L5

1 Jake has frogs and fish in his garden pond.
He took a sample from the pond and counted the number of frogs and fish.
The percentage bar chart shows his results.

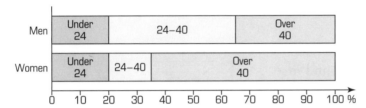

FROGS   FISH

0%   50%   100%

a What was the approximate percentage of fish in Jake's sample? 43 %.
b Jake took a second sample and found there were 12 frogs and 38 fish.
Draw a percentage bar chart to show the results from this second sample.

2 The bar chart shows the ages of employees in a company.

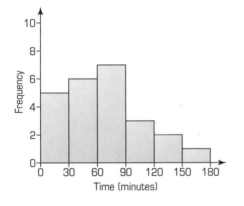

a What percentage of men who work for the company are aged 24–40?
b There are 18 women aged 24–40 working for the company.
Find the total number of women who work for the company.
c Iain says that the same number of men and women under 24 work for the company.
Explain why he may not be correct.

L6

3 The frequency diagram shows times spent on the telephone one evening by a sample of students.

Nick said one phone call lasted over 150 minutes.
Explain why this statement may be false.

L7

4 Students in Years 10 and 11 at a school have opted to study History, Geography or both subjects.

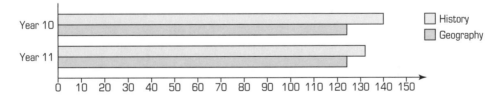

There are 240 students in each year group.

a How many students have opted to study both History and Geography in
  i Year 10   **ii** Year 11?
b How many students in total have opted to study History but not Geography?

► A **pie chart** uses a circle to display discrete data.
It compares the size of a category with the whole.

KEYWORDS
Pie chart   Estimate
Discrete   Frequency

example

There are 150 pupils in a school year.
65 of the pupils are boys.
Find the angle on the pie chart that
represents boys.

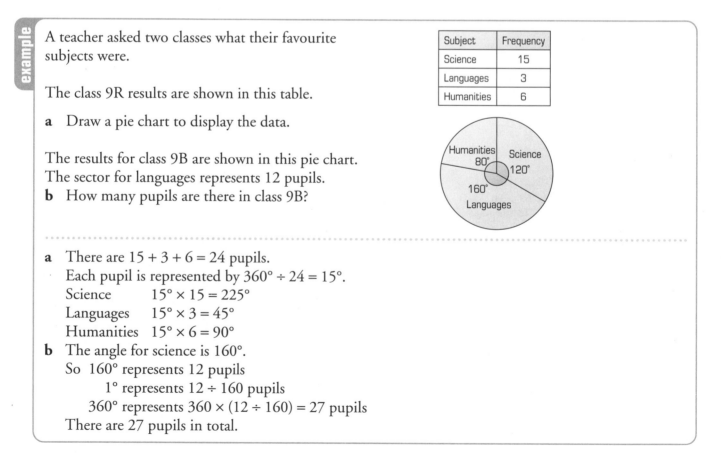

The angle is $\frac{65}{150} \times 360 = 156°$.

example

This pie chart shows the types of trees found in a
wood.

Estimate the percentage of oak trees in the wood.

About 30% are oak trees.

The whole pie represents the total frequency.
The angle at the centre of the circle is proportional to the frequency.

► One item is represented by (360° ÷ total frequency)

example

A teacher asked two classes what their favourite
subjects were.

The class 9R results are shown in this table.

Subject	Frequency
Science	15
Languages	3
Humanities	6

a Draw a pie chart to display the data.

The results for class 9B are shown in this pie chart.
The sector for languages represents 12 pupils.
b How many pupils are there in class 9B?

a There are 15 + 3 + 6 = 24 pupils.
Each pupil is represented by 360° ÷ 24 = 15°.
Science   15° × 15 = 225°
Languages   15° × 3 = 45°
Humanities   15° × 6 = 90°
b The angle for science is 160°.
So 160° represents 12 pupils
1° represents 12 ÷ 160 pupils
360° represents 360 × (12 ÷ 160) = 27 pupils
There are 27 pupils in total.

Exercise D4

L5 [M] **1** In a survey people said whether or not they liked Japanese food.
The pie chart shows the results of the survey.
Estimate what percentage said they liked Japanese food. *28%*

[calc] **2** At a school students were asked to choose one option to study.
They had to choose between art, photography and music.
The table shows the choices made by a first year group.

Subject	Number
Art	25
Photography	60
Music	15

a Draw a pie chart to show the information in the table.
b The pie chart on the right shows the choices made by a second year group.
Danny said:

> 'More students in the first year group preferred photography.'

Explain why this statement is not necessarily correct.

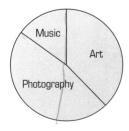

L6 [M] **3** Thirty out of 36 pupils said they watch *The Simpsons*.
What angle would show this on a pie chart?

[calc] **4** Class 9R were asked to state which sport they preferred to play in games.
They had to choose between football, hockey and rugby.
The table shows their preferences.

Sport	Number
Football	5
Hockey	9
Rugby	10

a Draw a pie chart to show this information.
Show your working and draw your angles accurately.
b Class 9B were also asked to state their preferred sport.
Their preferences are shown in the pie chart.
The sector for hockey represents 12 pupils.
How many pupils in total are there in class 9B?

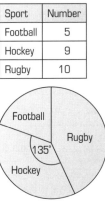

5 Six out of a class of twenty-four boys in a class at a school have blond hair.

a What angle would show this on a pie chart

Exactly one-quarter of the boys in this class also have blue eyes.
b From this information what percentage of the boys have blond hair and blue eyes?
Choose your answer from this list:
$6\frac{1}{4}$% $12\frac{1}{2}$%   25%   50%   Not possible to tell

L7 **6** Ravi drew this pie chart to show how much time, on average, he spends doing things on a school day.

a The sum of the sectors is not 100%.
Does this mean that there has been a mistake in the pie chart?
Explain your answer.
b Calculate how much time, on average, Ravi spends watching TV.
Give your answer in hours and minutes.

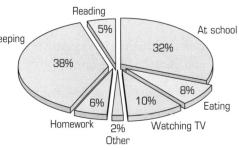

▶ A **line graph** for time series shows how something changes over time. Time is always on the horizontal axis.

KEYWORDS
Line graph   Time series

example

The graph shows the maximum and minimum midday temperatures in Paris over the last year.

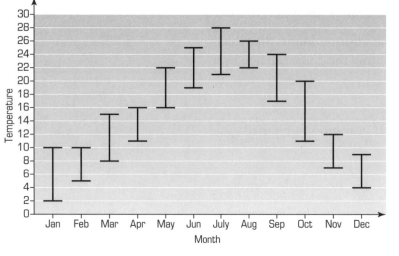

a In which month did Paris have the smallest range in temperature?
b In July the temperature range was 7°. Which other two months had a temperature range of 7°?

··

a August, as it has the shortest bar.
b March and September

Points on the graph can be joined to compare trends over time.

example

The diagram shows data about the number of supermarkets in a town open for 24 hours over the Christmas period.

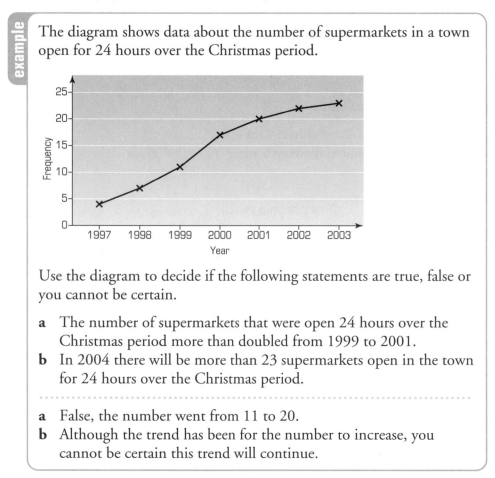

Use the diagram to decide if the following statements are true, false or you cannot be certain.

a The number of supermarkets that were open 24 hours over the Christmas period more than doubled from 1999 to 2001.
b In 2004 there will be more than 23 supermarkets open in the town for 24 hours over the Christmas period.

··

a False, the number went from 11 to 20.
b Although the trend has been for the number to increase, you cannot be certain this trend will continue.

Exercise D5

L5

1 The graph shows the average weights of baby boys and girls.

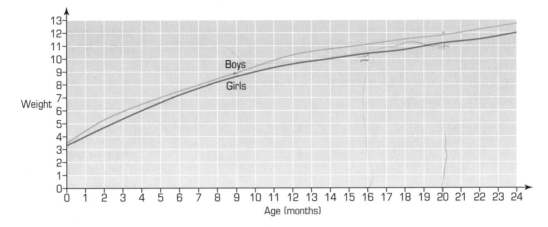

a What is the average weight of:
  i a boy aged 20 months **ii** a girl aged 16 months?

b Jim is of average weight for his age. He weighs 9 kg.
Use the graph to find Jim's age.

The table shows how much a baby girl weighs, on average, every
6 months for the first 2 years. It also shows her increase in weight.

Age (months)	Weight at start, kg	Weight at end, kg	Approximate weight gain, kg
0–6	3.3	7.2	3.9
6–12	7.2		
12–18			
18–24			

c Use the graph to complete the table.

L6

2 The graph shows the number
of mature students attending
Townly University.
Use the diagram to decide
whether or not the following
statements are true,
false or you cannot be certain.
In each case explain your answer.

a The number of mature students attending Townly University in 2003 was 400.

b The number of mature students at Townly University fell by more than two-thirds from
1984 to 1994.

c There were fewer students in total at Townly University in 1996 than in 1990.

3 The graphs shows the temperature
taken at hourly intervals of a
hospital patient.

a Estimate the temperature of the
patient at:
  i 6.30 am   **ii** 10.30 am

b Explain why your answers can
only be estimates.

► A **scatter graph** is useful for comparing two sets of data with each other.
Plotted points are not joined on a scatter graph.

KEYWORDS
Scatter graph   Correlation
Relationship   Line of best fit

If the points lie roughly in a straight line, there is a relationship or **correlation** between the variables.

positive   negative   no correlation

If the points go upwards there is **positive correlation**.
If they go downwards there is **negative correlation**.

If a graph shows correlation then you can draw a **line of best fit**.

► The line of best fit should pass as closely as possible through the points.

► There should be about the same number of points above the line as there are below it.

► The line does not have to pass through (0, 0).

example

The scatter graph shows the daily maximum temperatures and heating costs of a house for the first day of each month over a year.
The diagram also shows a line of best fit for this data.

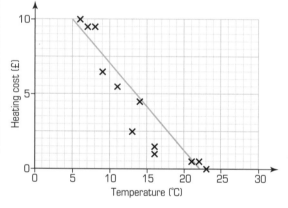

a Describe the relationship shown by the scatter graph.
b Use the line of best fit to estimate the heating cost when the temperature is 14 °C.
c One day the heating costs were £6.50.
Estimate the temperature on that day.

Make sure you can read the scale on the *y*-axis:
10 squares represent £5.
1 square represents 50p.

a As the temperature increases the heating costs decrease.
b It will cost about £4.70.
c It must have been about 11 °C.

Exercise D6

L6

1 In a competition three games, X, Y and Z, are played.
The scatter graphs show the scores of all competitors that played
all three games.

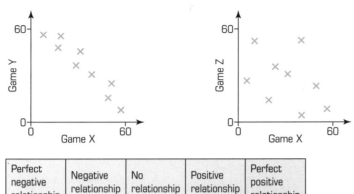

Perfect negative relationship	Negative relationship	No relationship	Positive relationship	Perfect positive relationship

Perfect means the points
lie exactly on a line.

a Choose from the statements above the one that best describes
the relationship between:
i game X and game Y **ii** game X and game Z.

b What can you tell about the relationship between Game Y and
Game Z?
Sketch a scatter graph showing this relationship. Remember to
label the axes.

2 Here are some false statements about lines of best fit that can be
drawn on scatter graphs.
Explain why they are false and suggest an alternative statement.

a Lines of best fit must always pass through the origin.
b Lines of best fit should join all the points together.
c Lines of best fit should always slope upwards.

L7

3 The scatter graph shows the diameter and
height of a sample of pine trees.
a Describe what the scatter graph shows
about the diameter and
height of pine trees.
b Copy the graph and draw a line of best fit.
c Use the line to estimate the height of a
pine tree with diameter 20 cm.
d Another tree has diameter 10 cm and height 14 m.
Use the graph to explain whether or not you think this is a pine tree.

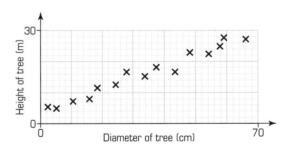

4 The diagram shows the correlation between engine
capacity (in cm³) and urban fuel consumption (in miles
per gallon) of a sample of cars.

a Describe the relationship shown by the scatter graph.
b Use the line of best fit to estimate the urban fuel
consumption of a car with engine capacity:
i 2000 cm³
ii 3500 cm³
c Use the line of best fit to estimate the engine capacity
of a car with urban fuel consumption of:
i 35 mpg
ii 10 mpg

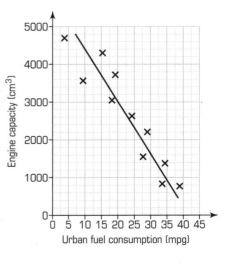

Probability problems and mutually exclusive events

▶ **Probability** is a measure of how likely an event is to happen.

▶ Probabilities are measured on a scale from 0 to 1.
They can be given as fractions, decimals or percentages.

p(A) is a shorthand way of writing 'the probability of event A happening'.

When **outcomes** are **equally likely**:

▶ $p(A) = \dfrac{\text{number of ways A can occur}}{\text{total possible number of outcomes}}$

▶ $p(\text{not A}) = 1 - p(A)$

If you know the probability of an event, you can estimate how many times it is likely to occur.

▶ Expected frequency = probability × number of trials

---

example

This is a fair six-sided spinner.

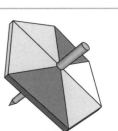

a There are only 3 colours, but the probability of white is not $\frac{1}{3}$.
Explain why not.
b Write down the probability that the spinner lands on   **i** blue   **ii** not blue.
c The spinner is spun 30 times. How many times would you expect it to land on white?

....

a Only 1 out of 6 sections is white.
The spinner is fair so all sections are equally likely, giving p(white) = $\frac{1}{6}$.
b **i** $\frac{3}{6} = \frac{1}{2}$ **ii** $1 - \frac{1}{2} = \frac{1}{2}$
c Expected frequency = $\frac{1}{6} \times 30 = 5$ times

---

example

There are green and blue counters in a box.
The probability that I choose a green counter is $\frac{1}{5}$.
The first 2 counters that I choose are green.
What is the smallest number of blue counters that could be in the bag?

....

Assume the 2 green counters chosen are the only green counters.
Then p(G) = $\frac{1}{5} = \frac{2}{10}$, converting to a fraction with numerator 2.
If 2 out of 10 are green, $10 - 2 = 8$ may be blue.
So the smallest possible number of blue counters is 8.

Mutually exclusive events cannot occur at the same time.

▶ The sum of all mutually exclusive events is 1.

---

example

There are orange (O), lemon (L) and strawberry (S) sweets in a bag.
p(O) = $\frac{5}{12}$ p(L) = $\frac{1}{6}$ p(S) = $\frac{1}{4}$
Are there any other flavour sweets in the bag? Explain your answer.

....

$\frac{5}{12} + \frac{1}{6} + \frac{1}{4} = \frac{5}{12} + \frac{2}{12} + \frac{3}{12} = \frac{10}{12} \neq 1$
There must be another flavour sweet in the bag to make the total probability 1.

Exercise D7

L5

1 There are five numbered discs in a bag. One disc is chosen at random.
The probability that the disc has a prime number on it is $\frac{2}{5}$.
Three of the discs are numbered 1, 3 and 6.
What numbers might be on the other discs? *4 5*

2 A family pack of crisps contains 25 bags with various flavours.

Flavour	Ready Salted	Salt & Vinegar	Cheese & Onion	Smokey Bacon	Barbecue Beef	Prawn Cocktail
Number	6	5	5	4	2	3

a What flavour bag could I choose if the probability of it being chosen is $\frac{1}{5}$? *Ready Salted*
b What is the probability of choosing Salt & Vinegar flavour crisps? *$\frac{5}{25}$*

Jenny eats a bag of Salt & Vinegar crisps.
She then chooses another bag at random.
c Work out the probability that Prawn Cocktail is chosen. *$\frac{3}{24}$*

3 There are three teams that play football for Warren football club.
Under 8s play 5-a-side, Under 11s play 7-a-side; Under 14s play 11-a-side.
One Saturday each team has the exact number of players it needs.
One of these players is chosen as 'Player of the Week'.
a Jordan says that there are only 3 teams so the probability that a player from the Under 8s is chosen must be $\frac{1}{3}$. Explain why Jordan is wrong.
b What is the probability that a player in the Under 8s team is chosen? *$\frac{1}{5}$ because there are only 5 players*

L6

4 There are some marbles in a bag. They are either blue or green.
The probability that a blue marble is chosen is $\frac{1}{8}$.
a What is the probability of choosing a green marble?

One marble is taken out of the bag. It is blue.
b What is the smallest number of green marbles there could be in the bag?

Another marble is taken out of the bag. It is also blue.
c Using this extra information, what is the smallest number of green marbles there could be in the bag?

5 The probability that Rita wins a game of noughts and crosses is 0.64.
Is she more likely to win or lose the game? Explain how you know. *She will win because .64 is closer to 1 than .36*

6 Chelsea is either early for school, on time or late.
The table shows some of the probabilities of each of these occurring on a school day.
a What is the probability that Chelsea is late for school on a school day? *$\frac{1}{3}$*

Event	Probability
Early	0.42
On time	0.38
Late	

There are 190 school days in a year.
b What is the expected number of times that Chelsea will not be late for school during one school year?

L7 **M**

7 I am going to take a marble from a large bag of marbles.
The probability that the marble is yellow is $\frac{1}{3}$.
There are 7 yellow marbles in the bag.
How many marbles are there in the bag that are not yellow? *14*

8 In a guessing game the probability that Jim wins is 0.45.
Jim plays the game 40 times.
How many times does he expect to win?

9 Imogen plays Scrabble with a friend. She wins 18 of the games that she plays.
She estimates that the probability of winning is 0.4.
How many games of scrabble did Imogen play in total?

In probability you need to list all the possible outcomes systematically.

KEYWORDS
Independent   Event
Outcome
Sample space diagram

example

Four friends, Ann (A), Ben (B), Carl (C) and Dave (D) have three tickets to a football match.
List the different groups of three that can go to the match.

List the possibilities systematically: ABC, ABD, ACD, BCD.

example

Joe has two coins in his pocket, 10p and 2p.
Kath has three coins in her pocket, 20p, 10p and 2p.
They each choose one coin. Each coin is equally likely to be chosen.

a   List the ways in which the coins can be chosen.
b   What is the probability that they both choose coins of the same value?

a

Joe	10	10	10	2	2	2
Kath	20	10	2	20	2	10

b   p(both 10p or both 2p) = $\frac{2}{6} = \frac{1}{3}$

You can use a **sample space diagram** to list the outcomes of two events.

example

Two 4-sided dice are each numbered 1, 2, 3, 4.
The dice are rolled and their scores are added together.
Draw a sample space diagram to show all possible outcomes.
What is the probability of getting a total of 6?

There are 16 outcomes and 3 totals of 6.
p(6) = $\frac{3}{16}$

+	1	2	3	4
1	2	3	4	5
2	3	4	5	6
3	4	5	6	7
4	5	6	7	8

example

The table shows the different flavours of sweets in two bags.
One sweet is chosen at random.

Flavour / Bag	A	B
Lemon	12	7
Orange	4	5
Strawberry	9	8

a   Find the probability that the sweet is orange.

The sweet is taken from bag B.
b   Find the probability that the sweet is lemon.

There are 25 sweets in bag A, and 20 in bag B.
a $\frac{9}{45} = \frac{1}{5}$ b $\frac{7}{20}$

▶   Two events are **independent** if the outcome of one event does not affect the outcome of the other event.

Flipping a coin, then rolling a dice are independent events, because the outcome on the coin doesn't affect the score on the dice.

Exercise D8

L5 **M** **1** James rolls a fair dice. He gets a 5. James rolls the dice again.
What is the probability that he will get a 5 again?

2 Tom, Dick and Harry go on a helter-skelter ride at a funfair.
Write out all the possible orders in which they can go down the helter-skelter.

3 Two 4-sided dice numbered 1, 2, 3, 4 are thrown.
The numbers on the dice are multiplied.
The table shows all the possible answers.
What is the probability that the answer is:

+	1	2	3	4
1	1	2	3	4
2	2	4	6	8
3	3	6	9	12
4	4	8	12	16

a greater than 4   **b** an odd number?

L6 **4** Jenny has two coins, a 20p and a 50p.
Inzimam has three coins, a 10p, a 20p, and a 50p.
They each choose one of their own coins. Each coin is equally likely to be chosen.

a List the different ways in which the coins might be chosen.
b What is the probability that they choose coins of different value?

5 The PIN code for a mobile phone contains the four digits 2, 2, 5 and 8.
List all the different possible combinations for the PIN code.

6 Two spinners have three equal sectors.
Each spinner is spun.
The numbers showing are added to get a total.
List all the possible totals.
What is the probability that the total is:

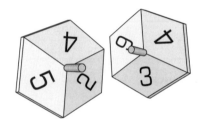

a 5   **b** 8   **c** less than 4?

L7 **7** The table shows information about some students in a year group.

	Blonde	Brunette
Blue-eyed	20	12
Brown-eyed	7	11

One student is chosen at random.
What is the probability that the student is:
a brown-eyed   **b** a brunette   **c** a blue-eyed blonde?

8 A set of cards, with one maths question on each card, is categorised by
question type and level of difficulty.
The table shows the probability of selecting a card at random.

	Number	Algebra	Shape	Data
Easy	0.2	0.25	0.15	0.05
Difficult	0.05	0.1	0.2	

One card is taken at random from the set.

a What is the probability that it is:
   i an algebra question   **ii** an easy question?

There are 60 questions in the set.
b How many of these are: **i** number questions   **ii** difficult questions?

9 Three coins are thrown.

a List all the different possible outcomes.

Three coins are thrown 200 times.

b What is the expected number of times that you would get two tails and one head?

Relative frequency

When you do not know the theoretical probability of an event you can estimate it by carrying out an experiment.

KEYWORDS
Experiment   Biased
Relative frequency Trial
Experimental probability

▶ Relative frequency or experimental probability

$$= \frac{\text{number of successful trials}}{\text{total number of trials}}$$

▶ The more **trials** you carry out the more reliable your estimate will be.

example

Five students carried out an experiment to find out whether a spinner is biased.
The spinner has four sides coloured black, blue, grey and white.
Their results are summarised in the table.

Pupil	Number of spins	Black	Blue	Grey	White
A	40	8	16	10	6
B	50	12	14	11	13
C	100	27	29	25	19
D	10	2	4	2	2
E	50	9	14	13	14

a Which student's data should give the best estimates for experimental probability?
Explain your answer.

The students collected all their results together in this table.

Colour	Black	Blue	Grey	White
Frequency	58	77	61	54

b Write down whether you think the spinner is biased.
Explain your answer.
c What is the probability that the spinner lands on
i blue   **ii** white?

....

a C because he/she did the most spins.
b If the spinner is fair each colour should have come up about the same number of times.
Blue came up more than the other colours, so the spinner may be biased.
c i $\frac{77}{250}$ **ii** $\frac{54}{250}$

▶ A piece of apparatus is **biased** if the experimental probabilities, based on a large number of trials, are very different from the theoretical probabilities.

Dice, counters and spinners are all examples of apparatus.

Exercise D9

L6

1 Four students carried out an experiment to see if a coin was biased.
The data they collected is shown in the table.

	Lauren	Charlie	Robert	Luke
Heads	26	111	10	249
Tails	24	109	10	261

a Whose data is likely to give the most reliable answer to whether or not the coin is biased?
Explain your answer.

The students collected their data together in this table.

Heads	396
Tails	404

b Consider the data.
Write down whether or not you think the coin is biased or not, and explain your answer.
c Use the data to work out the probability of the coin showing tails.

2 A bag contains a large number of seeds that are purple or white.
Rachel and Lorna each select 100 seeds at random.
Each seed is returned to the bag before another is selected.
These are their results

	Purple	White
Rachel	59	41
Lorna	44	56

a Write down the relative frequencies of purple and white seeds for Rachel and Lorna.
b Work out the relative frequency of purple and white seeds for their combined results.
c Which relative frequencies are likely to be the most accurate estimate of the probability that a selected seed is purple or white?
d If there are 10 000 seeds in the bag, estimate the number of purple seeds.

L7

3 Luke carries out an experiment with a group of 10 coins.
He drops the coins and notes how many of them show tails.
He repeats this experiment 12 times.

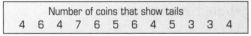

Number of coins that show tails
4 6 4 7 6 5 6 4 5 3 3 4

a Use Luke's data to work out the probability that a single coin when dropped will show tails.
Show your working.

Luke continues the experiment until he has dropped the group of 10 coins 40 times.

> See D7 for expected frequency.

b About how many of the coins in total would you expect to show tails?

4 A chef records the number of eggs that contain double yolks in each box he uses.
(Each box contains 6 eggs.)

Number of double yolks	0	1	2	3	4	5	6
Number of boxes	4	4	5	8	7	3	1

Work out the probability that the next box of 6 eggs the chef opens will contain:

a 6 eggs with double yolks
b 3 or 4 eggs with double yolks.

L5

1   A newspaper predicts what the ages of school teachers will be in six year's time. They print this chart.

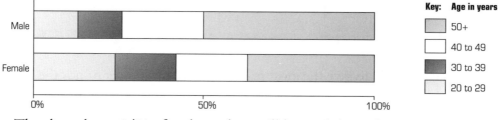

a The chart shows **24%** of male teachers will be aged 40 to 49.
About what percentage of female teachers will be aged 40 to 49?

b About what percentage of female teachers will be aged **50+**?

c The newspaper predicts there will be about **20 000** male teachers aged 40 to 49.
Estimate the number of male teachers that will be aged 50+.

d Assume the total number of male teachers will be about the same as the total number of female teachers.
Use the chart to decide which statement is correct, A or B.

A: Generally, male teachers will tend to be younger than female teachers.
B: Generally, female teachers will tend to be younger than male teachers.

Explain how you used the chart to decide.

2   These pie charts show the area of the Earth's surface covered by water and land north and south of the equator.

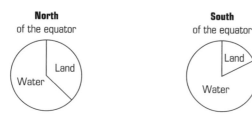

a About what percentage of the Earth's surface **north** of the equator is covered by **land**?

b About what percentage of the Earth's surface **south** of the equator is covered by **land**?

c Sketch a pie chart to show the area of the **whole** Earth's surface covered by water and by land.
Label the parts of your pie chart **Water** and **Land**.

L6

3   **a** A bag has **20** cubes in it. **6** of the cubes are green.
You take one cube out of the bag at random.
Write down the four values below that show the **probability** that you take out a cube that is green.

$\frac{6}{14}$ 30%   0.6 $\frac{3}{10}$ 6% $\frac{3}{5}$

$\frac{6}{20}$ 0.03   0.3 $\frac{6}{10}$ 60% $\frac{6}{26}$

b A box has **20** counters in it. **11** of the counters are red.
You take one counter out of the box at random.

   i What is the probability that the counter you take out is **not** red?
Write your answer as a **fraction**.

   ii Now write your answer as a **percentage**.

L6   **4**   The scatter diagram shows the heights and masses of some horses.
The scatter diagram also shows a line of best fit.

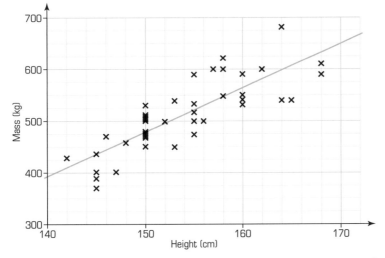

a   What does the scatter diagram show about the **relationship** between the height and
    mass of horses?

b   The **height** of a horse is **163 cm**.
    Use the line of best fit to estimate the mass of the horse.

c   A different horse has a **mass of 625 kg**.
    Use the line of best fit to estimate the height of the horse.

d   A teacher asks his class to investigate this statement:
    'The length of the **back leg** of a horse is **always less than** the length of the **front
    leg** of a horse.'
    What might a scatter graph look like if the statement is correct?
    Illustrate your answer with a sketch.

L7   **5**   Some pupils threw 3 fair dice.
They recorded how many times
the numbers on the dice were
the same.

Name	Number of throws	Results		
		all different	2 the same	all the same
Morgan	40	26	12	2
Sue	140	81	56	3
Zenta	20	10	10	0
Ali	100	54	42	4

a   Write the name of the pupil whose data are **most likely** to give the best estimate of
    the probability of getting each result. Explain your answer.

b   This table shows the pupils' results
    collected together:

Number of throws	Results		
	all different	2 the same	all the same
300	171	120	9

Use these data to estimate the
probability of throwing numbers
that are **all different**.

c   The theoretical probability of each
    result is shown:

	all different	2 the same	all the same
Probability	$\frac{5}{9}$	$\frac{5}{12}$	$\frac{1}{36}$

Use these probabilities to
calculate, for 300 throws, **how many times** you would theoretically expect to get
each result.

d   Explain why the pupils' results are not the same as the theoretical results.

e   Jenny throws the 3 dice twice.
    Calculate the probability that she gets **all the same** on her first throw and gets **all
    the same** on her second throw.
    Show your working.

► This test is 1 hour long.
► You **must not** use a calculator for any question in this test.
► You will need: pen, pencil, rubber, ruler, paper and graph paper.

1 The diagram shows two straight lines.

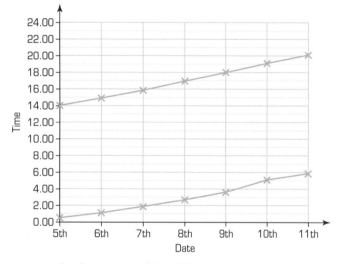

The two lines have no point of intersection (the lines never cross).

a Copy and complete the sentence:

When two straight lines have no point of intersection, the lines are _____.   (1 *mark*)

b Draw three straight lines that have exactly two points of intersection.   (1 *mark*)

2 The graph shows the times of high tide for a week in May for a town in Cornwall.

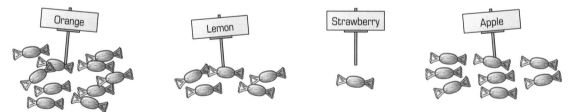

a On which date was the difference between the high tide times the greatest?   (1 *mark*)
b Write the times of high tide on this date.   (1 *mark*)

3 I buy a bag of orange, lemon, strawberry and apple flavour sweets.

There are 24 sweets altogether.
I take one sweet from the bag.
Each sweet is equally likely to be chosen.

What is the probability that the sweet chosen is:
a strawberry
b apple
c not apple?   (3 *marks*)

4 You can buy a DVD player for £99.
In 2001 the same DVD player would have cost 2.5 times as much as it costs now.
How much did the same DVD player cost in 2001?   (*2 marks*)

5 The graph shows the charges made by an IT firm for its time.

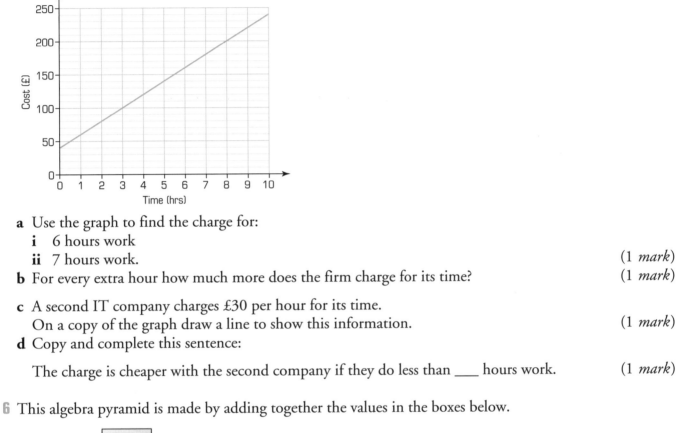

a Use the graph to find the charge for:
  i   6 hours work
  ii   7 hours work.   (*1 mark*)
b For every extra hour how much more does the firm charge for its time?   (*1 mark*)

c A second IT company charges £30 per hour for its time.
On a copy of the graph draw a line to show this information.   (*1 mark*)
d Copy and complete this sentence:

The charge is cheaper with the second company if they do less than ___ hours work.   (*1 mark*)

6 This algebra pyramid is made by adding together the values in the boxes below.

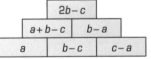

a Copy and complete this pyramid using the values:
   $a = 2$ $b = 7$ $c = 3$

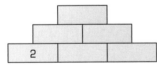

     (*2 marks*)

b I use different values to complete the pyramid.
What values for *a*, *b* and *c* did I use?

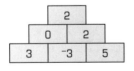

     (*2 marks*)

7 This diagram can help you work out some fraction calculations.

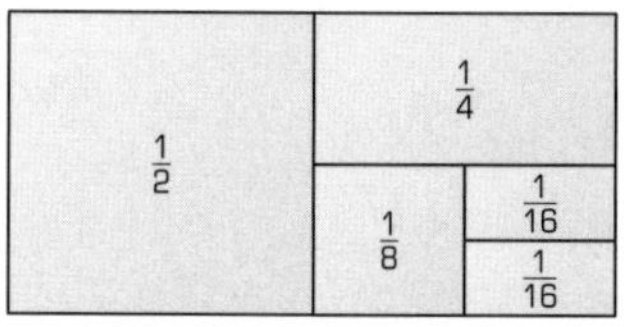

Calculate:

a $\frac{1}{2} + \frac{1}{16}$ **b** $\frac{1}{4} + \frac{1}{8}$ **c** $\frac{1}{4} - \frac{1}{16}$ (3 *marks*)

8 **a** A function maps the number n to the number $n - 1$.
Copy and complete the missing values:

$$\begin{array}{ccc} n & \rightarrow & n - 1 \\ 4 & \rightarrow & \underline{} \\ \underline{} & \rightarrow & 24 \end{array}$$

(1 *mark*)

b A different function maps the number n to $3n$.
Copy and complete the missing values:

$$\begin{array}{ccc} n & \rightarrow & 3n \\ 4 & \rightarrow & \underline{} \\ \underline{} & \rightarrow & 24 \end{array}$$

(1 *mark*)

c Many different functions can map the number 16 to the number 4.
Copy and complete the tables by writing two different functions.

$$\begin{array}{ccc} n & \rightarrow & \underline{} \\ 16 & \rightarrow & 4 \end{array} \qquad \begin{array}{ccc} n & \rightarrow & \underline{} \\ 16 & \rightarrow & 4 \end{array}$$

(2 *marks*)

9 You can make three different cuboids using 8 cubes.

		Dimensions		
Cuboid A	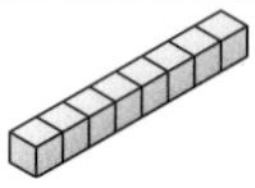	1	1	8
Cuboid B		1	2	4
Cuboid C		2	2	2

a Which of the cuboids has the smallest surface area?
Explain how you know. (2 *marks*)
b Which cuboid has the largest volume?
Explain how you know. (2 *marks*)
c How many of cuboid B would you need to make a $4 \times 4 \times 4$ cube? (1 *mark*)
d You can make four different cuboids with 12 cubes.
What are the dimensions of each cuboid? (3 *marks*)

10 These shapes are drawn on square grids.

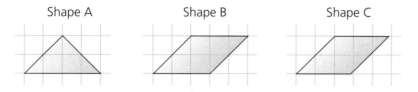

Shape A   Shape B   Shape C

    a What type of triangle is shape A?   (*1 mark*)
    b Is shape B a parallelogram? Explain how you know.   (*1 mark*)
    c Is shape C a square? Explain how you know.   (*1 mark*)

11 Copy the table and write in the missing numbers.
The first row is done for you.

1st Number	2nd Number	Sum	Difference
9	4	13	5
7	⁻2		
3		⁻1	

(*2 marks*)

12 a Calculate $\frac{4}{9} \times \frac{3}{4}$. Show your working.
      Write your answer as a fraction in its simplest form.   (*2 marks*)
   b In a school sixth form, two thirds are female.
      One fifth of these females wear glasses.
      What fraction of the sixth form are females that wear glasses?   (*1 mark*)

13 a Rearrange the equations:
      i $x + 7 = y$ $x =$ _____
      ii $5x = y$ $x =$ _____
      iii $x - 6 = 12y$ $x =$ _____   (*3 marks*)
   b Rearrange this equation to make x the subject:
      $4(3 + x) = y$ (*2 marks*)

14 Two people travel from A to B along different routes.

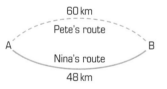

Their journeys take the same amount of time.
Pete travels at an average of 40 km/h.
What is Nina's average speed?   (*2 marks*)

15 a Which of the following expressions is the same as $x^2 + 5x - 6$?

$(x + 2)(x - 3)$ $(x - 3)(x - 2)$ $(x + 1)(x - 6)$ $(x - 1)(x + 6)$

(*1 mark*)

   b Multiply out the expression $(x + 4)(x + 5)$.
      Write your answer as simply as possible.   (*2 marks*)

16 The scatter graph shows the average wingspan and the average
body length of different species of birds.

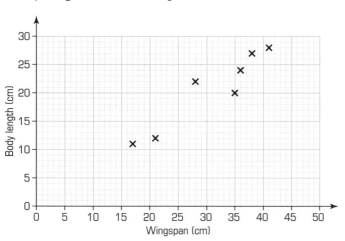

a What does the scatter graph tell you about the type of correlation between average
  wingspan and body length of this sample of birds? (1 *mark*)
b Copy the graph and draw a line of best fit. (1 *mark*)
c If the wingspan increased by 10 cm, by how much would you expect the body
  length to increase by? (1 *mark*)
d A bird has a wingspan of 47 cm and body length 11 cm.
  Is it likely to be one of this species of bird? (1 *mark*)

17 I have two fair four-sided dice.

One dice is numbered 2, 3, 5, 7
The other is numbered 1, 2, 4, 8

I throw both dice and add the scores.
What is the probability that the total is odd?
You must show working to explain your answer. (2 *marks*)

18 The table shows a recipe for fruit punch.

Juice	Amount
Orange	$\frac{3}{8}$ litre
Lime	$\frac{1}{8}$ litre
Lemonade	$\frac{1}{2}$ litre
Total	1 litre

I want to make $2\frac{1}{2}$ litres of the same drink.
How much of each type of drink should I use? (3 *marks*)

19 Think about rectangles that have:

- a perimeter of 14 cm
- each side is a whole number of centimetres

Prove that there are only three of these rectangles. (3 *marks*)

▶ This test is 1 hour long.
▶ You may use a calculator for any question in this test.
▶ You will need: pen, pencil, rubber, ruler, compasses, calculator, paper and graph paper.

1 Look at this shape made from eight cubes.

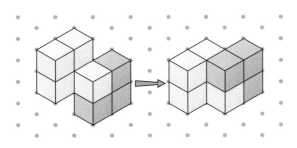

Five cubes are white. Three cubes are blue.
Part of the shape is rotated through 90° to make the new shape.
After another rotation of 90°, the shape is a cube.
Draw this cube.   (2 *marks*)

2 The graph shows information about the minimum and maximum temperatures
in Madrid in 2003.

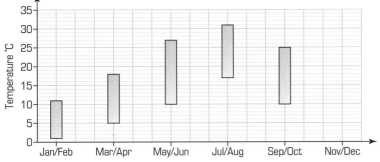

a What is the maximum temperature during March and April?   (1 *mark*)
b In November and December the minimum temperature is 2°C.
The range in temperature is 11°C.
Copy the graph and draw a bar to show this information.   (2 *marks*)

3 a A student measured the angles in a quadrilateral.
He said: The angles are 40°, 70°, 120° and 140°.
Could he be correct?   (1 *mark*)
b This diagram is not drawn accurately.
Calculate the size of angle *x*.
Show your working.   (2 *marks*)

4 a Explain why 24 is not a prime number.   (1 *mark*)
b The numbers in the 4 times table are 4, 8, 12, 16, ...
Explain why there will never be a prime number in the 4 times table. (1 *mark*)
c The numbers in the 5 times table are 5, 10, 15, 20, ...
Explain why there will only be one prime number in the 5 times table. (1 *mark*)

5 A box contains bags of sweets.
Each bag of sweets weighs 125 grams.
Altogether the bags of sweets inside a box weigh 3 kg.
How many bags of sweets are there inside the box?   (1 *mark*)

6 a Draw a quadrilateral that has two pairs of equal and opposite sides. (1 *mark*)
  b Draw a quadrilateral that has two pairs of equal and adjacent sides. (1 *mark*)

7 Cooking temperatures in a cookery book are given in Fahrenheit, °F.
To change the cooking temperature to Centigrade, °C:

  Subtract 32 from °F, then multiply by 5 and divide by 9,
  then round your answer to the nearest 10.

Would the cooking temperatures 350°F and 360°F have the same cooking temperature in °C?
Show your working to explain your answer. (3 *marks*)

8 a The square and the rectangle below have the same area.

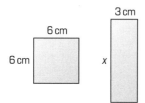

  Work out the value of *x*. (1 *mark*)
  b The triangle and the square below have the same area.

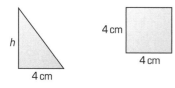

  Work out the value of *h*. Show your working. (2 *marks*)

9 a How much is 23% of £3765? (2 *marks*)
  b What percentage is £1280 of £3765?
  Show your working and give your answer to the nearest whole number. (2 *marks*)

10 The graph shows a straight line.

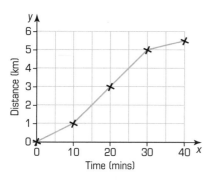

  a Write down the coordinates of three points that lie on the line. (1 *mark*)
  b Write an equation of the straight line. (1 *mark*)
  c On a similar graph, draw the straight line that has the equation $x + y = 2$. (1 *mark*)

11 There are 12 questions in a quiz.
A correct answer scores 3 points. An incorrect answer loses 2 points.
A question not answered scores nothing. It is possible to have a negative total.

   a What are the maximum and minimum points that you could score on the quiz? *(1 mark)*

   b A student answers 10 of the questions. 4 are correct.
Explain why this student's total is zero. *(1 mark)*

   c Write down three different ways in which a student could have a total score of 6 points. *(2 marks)*

12 a The cross-section of a cylindrical tube is a circle.
The radius of this circle is 5 cm.
What is the area of this circle? *(1 mark)*

   b I can fill the tube with 550 cm^3 of water.
What is the height of the tube? Give your answer to the nearest whole number. *(2 marks)*

13 a Use the formula $y = \dfrac{x+2}{3x}$ to find the value of y when $x = 7$. *(2 marks)*

   b Use the same formula to find the value of x when $y = \frac{1}{2}$. *(2 marks)*

14 A teacher asked a class of students what mobile phone network they use.
The pie chart shows the results.

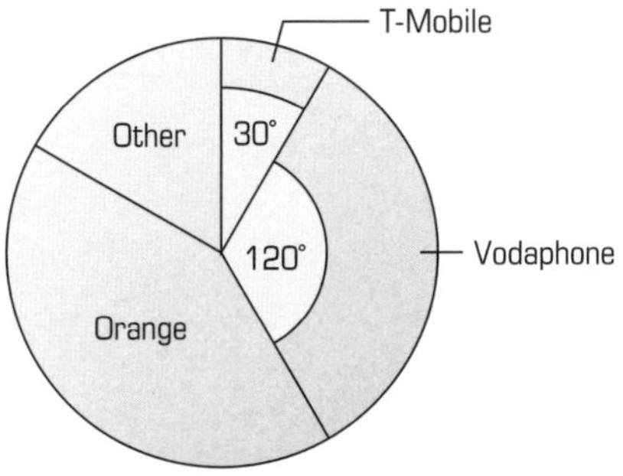

   a 4 students use T-mobile.
How many students use Vodafone? *(2 marks)*

   b In another class there were 32 students.
The teacher asked this class what mobile phone network they use.
6 students use Orange.
On a pie chart what would be the angle for the sector Orange? *(2 marks)*

15 One shade of brown paint is made by mixing red, yellow and blue paints in the ratio 3 : 4 : 1.

   a In one pot of paint the amount of red paint used is 120 ml.
How much of the other two paint colours are used? *(1 mark)*

   b In a small paint pot, 10 ml of yellow paint is used.
How much of the other two paint colours are used? *(2 marks)*

16 I have 8 boxes of matches altogether.
The mean number of matches in the boxes is 44.
There are 3 boxes with 43 matches, 2 boxes with 44 matches, 1 box with 45 matches and 1 box with 48 matches.
How many matches are there in the eighth box? *(2 marks)*

17 The diagram shows a nonagon with 9 triangles.
It is constructed using 9 straight lines.

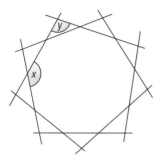

    a Without measuring, explain why angle *x* must be 140°.   *(1 mark)*
    b Calculate the size of angle *y*.
       You must show your working.   *(1 mark)*

    c Draw two points 5 cm apart, P and Q.
       Use compasses and straight edge to construct the perpendicular bisector of the line PQ.
       You must leave in your construction lines.   *(2 marks)*

18 Stuart uses an exercise bike to keep fit.
The simplified distance–time graph
shows how he used the machine during
one exercise session.

Use the graph to answer these questions.
    a Between the 10th and 20th minute of the cycle ride what was his speed in
       kilometres per hour?   *(1 mark)*
    b Throughout the cycle ride, for how many minutes did he travel at this speed?   *(1 mark)*
    c For the first 10 minutes his speed was slower.
       By how many kilometres per hour was his speed slower?   *(1 mark)*

19 Some numbers are smaller than their cubes.
For example: $2 < 2^3$
Which numbers are equal to their cubes?   *(2 marks)*

20 Is it possible to have a triangle with the angle and lengths shown below?

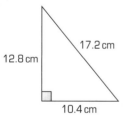

Show your calculations to support your answer.   *(2 marks)*

21 Look at these expressions.

What value of *x* makes the two expressions equal?
Show your working.   *(2 marks)*

Answers

Exercise N1

1 a 630 m **b** 220 m **c** 200 m **2** 2.51 km, 302 km **3** 165 m to 174 m

4 $29 \div 10 = 29 \times 0.1$ $29 \div 1000 = 29 \times 0.001$ **5 a** 29.5% **b** 23 128

6 a 10 **b** 0.01 **c** 0.01 **d i** $0.004 \times 0.01 = 0.000\,04$ **ii** $0.004 \div 10 = 0.004$
   e $2.5 + 10 = 12.5$ **f** $10 \times 0.2 \times 0.5 = 1$

7 Yes. The distance was measured to the nearest cm so it could have been up to 0.5 cm longer.

8 18.35 s to 18.45 s **9 a** 48.5% **b** 79

Exercise N2

1 42 **2 a** $^-9$ **b** 5 **3** 108 **4** 25, 30, 85 **5 a** 6 **b** $^-6 + ^-3 + ^-2 = ^-11$ **c** 5 and $^-2$

6 2 and 6, 3 and 4, or 12 and 1 **7 a** 5 **b** $^-2$ **c** $^-3 - (9) = ^-12$ **d** $^-3 - (^-6) = 3$

8 a e.g. $^-4 - ^-8 = 4$ **b** e.g. $^-6 - ^-2 = ^-4$ **9 a** 14 **b** 3, 13, 23, 31, 37, 39, 43 **10** $48 = 2 \times 2 \times 2 \times 2 \times 3$

11 $60 = 2 \times 2 \times 3 \times 5$

Exercise N3

1 343 **2** 40 000 **3** 7 **4** 100 **5** 5 **6 a** 3^4 **b** 2^5 **c** 3^4 and 9^2 **7** 5^3 **8** 3^5 **9** 7^9

10 3^6 **11 a** 8 **b** 1 **c** 1 **12** $k = 4$ **13** 65 536 **14** 8 **15** 256 **16** 10 000 000 000 **17** $x = 2, y = 4$

Exercise N4

1 a 100 **b** 100 **c** 90 **2 a** 25% **b** 70% **c** 40% **d** 62.5% **3 a** $\frac{1}{4}$ **b** $\frac{3}{5}$ **4** 5 **5 a** $\frac{11}{6}$ **b** $\frac{16}{27}$

6 $\frac{5}{8} = (\frac{100}{8} \times 3) = 62.5\%$ 62.5% is more than 58% so $\frac{5}{8}$ is larger.

7 $\frac{3}{8} = (\frac{100}{8} \times 3) = 37.5\%$ 37.5% is less than 38% so $\frac{3}{8}$ is smaller. **8 a** 10.5 **b** $2\frac{4}{10}$ or $\frac{24}{10}$

9 a $\frac{3}{8} \times \frac{1}{10} = \frac{3}{80}$ **b** $\frac{1}{2} + \frac{1}{10} + \frac{2}{5}$ **c** $\frac{4}{7}$ **10 a** $0.2 \times 0.25 = 0.05$ **b** $2 \div 0.2 = 10$

Exercise N5

1 44 **2 a** £4.80 **b** £8.05 **3** 228 **4** 60 **5** 1 : 3 **6** 30 **7 a** £20 : £30 **b** £80 : £64

8 93.75 calories **9 a** 6 : 5 **b** 7 : 6 **c** Joshua = 6 years old, Reuben = 3 years old

10 a 52% **b** 44.83% **c** tub: amount taken ÷ number sold = cost **11 a** 1.37 **b** 0.84 **12 a** £31.36 **b** £23.80

13 62 **14 a** £26.24 **b** 7 days **c** 10% of each new value is subtracted, not 10% of the original value.

Exercise N6

1 This answer is incorrect because 3×188 does not end in 5 or 0 but 16×35 does.

2 Because $\frac{10.5}{1.5} + \frac{7.5}{1.5} = 7 + 5$ **3 a** He didn't work out the denominator first. **b** 12 **4** 61 **5** 21

6 7 **7** 2 **8** 14 **9** $\frac{1}{3} + \frac{1}{4}$ is less than 1. When you divide by a number smaller than 1 you get a larger answer.

10 a 22 **b** 10 **11** 7.1 **12** $4\frac{2}{5}$ or 4.4 **13 a** 4 **b** 6 **14 a** 0.3 **b** 30 **15** 8.5 **16** 4.6

Exercise R1

1 a $\frac{1}{3}$ **b** 40% **c** Shape A **2 a** 200 g **b** 8 **c** 2 : 3 **3** 104

4 Various possible answers, e.g. $^-8 - ^-13$ and $^-6 - ^-1$ **5 a** $3^4, 3^4$ **b** $2^5, 2^7$

6 a 1 : 4 : 5 : 9 **b** 47.36842 Values from 47 to 48 are acceptable. **c** 1 : 3 : 8 : 6

7 a Yes **b** 14.55 s, 14.65 s **8 a** 0.00529 mm **b** 52 **9 a** 8 **b** 16 **c** 6 **d** Answer between 28 and 34

10 a $k = 3, m = 6$ **b** 16 384

Exercise N7

1 a 10% of 140 is 14 **b** 10% of 220 is 22
     5% of 140 is 7   5% of 220 is 11
     2.5% of 140 is 3.5   20% of 220 is 44
     so 17.5% of 140 = 14 + 7 + 3.5 = 24.5   so 35% of 220 = 22 + 11 + 44 = 77

2 a 372 **b** 50 **3** 1073 **4** 15 750 g or 15.74 kg **5** 8.5 m **6** 8.82 cm

7 a 31 302 **b** 3.1302 **c** 3130.2 **d** 740

8 10% of 485 = 48.5   20% of 485 = 97   1% of 485 = 4.85
   therefore 485 + 19% = 485 + 97 − 4.85 = 577.15

9 72 **10 b** 911 = 587 + 342 **c** 287 = 752 − 438 **11 a** $\frac{11}{30}$ **b** $\frac{1}{3} + \frac{1}{4}$ **c** $\frac{1}{4} + \frac{1}{252}$

12 Option **ii** involves paying less, by £8.

Exercise N8

1 9.1 **2** 10 **3 a** £117.80 **b** 29 **4 a** £390 **b** 500 **5 a** £156 **b** £3 **6** 80 **7** 3.2 **8** 340

9 60 **10 a** $76.32 \div 0.4 = 793.2 \div 4 = 190.8$ **b** $4.923 \div 0.05 = 492.3 \div 5 = 98.46$ **11** 560 **12** 470

Exercise N9

1 a i $(7.2 + 6.4 + 6.6 + 6.4) \div 4 \times 4.3 =$ **ii** 28.595
   b $42 \div 3.9 = 10.77$ (2 dp). The top mark possible is 10 so it is impossible for Jayne to get 42 with a difficulty rating of 3.9.

2 1.7 and 1.8 **3** x lies between 2.3 and 2.4

4 a $32 \div 5 \times 8 = 51.2$ km and $51.2 \div 13 = 3.938\,461\,538$ litres **b** 3.9 litres or 4 litres **5** $8\frac{1}{2}$ days old

1 b $11n$ **c** $3n+7$ **2 a** $5f+8$ **b** $9g+4$ **3** Add 5, add x, divide by 2, subtract 1.

4 a $n+9$ **b** $2n+5$ **5 a** $5a-3$ **b** $2b+8$ **c** $7c$ **6 a** $2n+24$ **b** $4n+12$

7 a $11x+7$ **b** $7x+14$ **c** $12x-11$ **d** x^2+6x+8 **e** $x^2+3x-10$ **f** x^2+2x+9

8 a a^7 **b** a^3b^2 **c** $6a^4b^2$ **d** a^7 **e** $4a^3$ **9 a** $12ab^3$ **b** $(5a^2)\div2$ **10** $\frac{b-a}{ab}$

11 a $4m+7n$ **b**

	$10m-n$	
$7m+n$		$3m-2n$
$5m+2n$	$2m-n$	$m-n$

Exercise A2

1 a 23 **b** 8 **c** 3 **2 a** 19 **b** 13 **c** 36 **3** $y=6$

4

x	$x-1$	$3x$	$3(x-1)$	$3x-1$
5	4	15	12	14
10	9	30	27	29
6	5	18	15	17

5 a $4n+3$ **b** Ian is not correct because if $4n+3=24$ then $4n=21$ and n is not a whole number.

6 $x=4$ **7 a** $2x+7=5x-2$ **b** $x=3$ **8 a** $x=12$ **b** $y=\frac{35}{2}$ **9** 7 **10** $22n$

11 a $x=\frac{-3}{2}$ **b** $x=4$ **12** $x=\frac{y-4}{3}$ **13** $x=a-\frac{y}{2}$ **14 a** 1.825 741 858 **b** 1.83, $^-$1.83 **15 a** 6.125 **b** 7.2

Exercise A3

1 a $^-$3 and 8 **b** $^-$8 and 3 **c** $^-$3 and $^-$6 **2 a** Ama is correct. **b** The answer is a recurring decimal, not an integer.

3 a $x=2$, $y=5$ and $x=3$, $y=11$ **b** $x=0.6$ or $x=^-1.6$ **4** 1.7 and 1.8 **5 a** 38 km/h **b** 49 km/h

Exercise R2

1 a ii Barry is one year younger than Tina. **iii** Carol is twice as old as Tina. **b** $n+4$, n, $2n+1$ **c i** 61 **ii** 62

2 $x-1\rightarrow5$, $2(x-1)\rightarrow10$, $x^2\rightarrow36$ **3 a** area $=15ab$, perimeter $=6a+10b$, or $2(3a+5b)$ **b** $4a$ and $3a$

4 a $3m-5=2m+3$ **b** $m=8$ **5** 49 **6 a** 4 **b** $7\frac{1}{2}$ **7 a** 13 403.07692 ... **b** 13 000

8 a i 1500 **ii** 20 **b** $\frac{3d}{5}$ **c i** $9x-14$ **ii** x^2+5x+6 **iii** x^2+3x-4 **iv** x^2-4x+4 **9 a i** is true. **b ii** is true.

10 a $^-$3, $^-$5, $^-$5 **b** 1.8

Exercise A4

1 a Double the previous number.

b Double the previous number (3, 6, 12, 24).

Add 3 each time (3, 6, 9, 12).

Add consecutive odd numbers starting with 3 (3, 6, 11, 18).

2 a 21 **b** 56 **c** $M=5H+1$

3 a i 1 black, 20 white **ii** 1 black, 36 white **iii** 1 black, $9P$ white **b** $T=4P-3$

4 a i 26, 31 **ii** Add 5 to the previous term. **b i** 37, 44 **ii** Add 7 to the previous term.

c i 17, 21 **ii** Add 4 to the previous term.

5 a $^-$2, 10 **b** 3 **6** $n^2=(n-1)^2+(n-1)+n=(n-1)^2+2n-1$

Exercise A5

1 a

Number of gym visits	0	5	10	15
Total cost (£)	0	18	36	54

b Points at (0, 0) (5, 18) (10, 36) (15, 54)

c

Number of gym visits	0	5	10	15
Total cost (£)	18	26	34	42

d

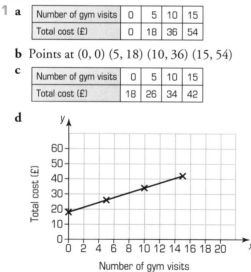

Points at (0, 18) (5, 26) (10, 34) (15, 54) **e** 9 visits

2

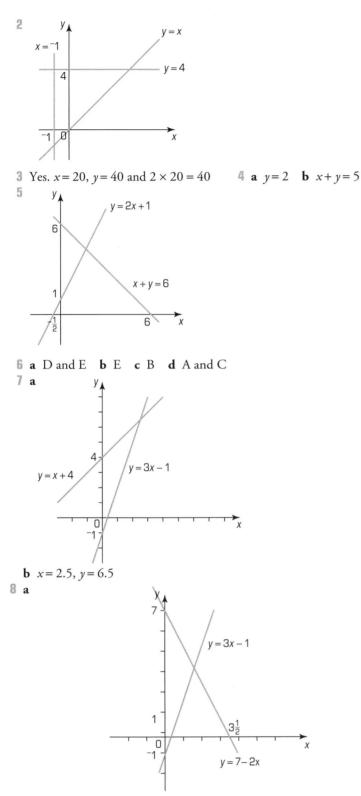

3 Yes. $x = 20$, $y = 40$ and $2 \times 20 = 40$ **4 a** $y = 2$ **b** $x + y = 5$

5

6 a D and E   **b** E   **c** B   **d** A and C

7 a

    b $x = 2.5$, $y = 6.5$

8 a

    b $x = 3$, $y = 1$

Exercise A6

1 a $320\,°F \approx 160\,°C$ **b** $280\,°F \approx 145\,°C$ **c** $350\,°F \approx 175\,°C$

2 a £10   **b** 0   **c i** On price plan A you pay 20p for each minute of calls.   **ii** On price plan B you pay 5p for each minute of calls plus £12.50 a month.   **d** When more than 75 minutes a month are used.

3 3, 4, 5, 6   **4** ⁻2, ⁻1, 0, 1, 2, 3, 4, 5, 6, 7, 8

5 a   **b** $x \geqslant 2$, $y \leqslant 5$, $x \leqslant 5$, $y \geqslant x$

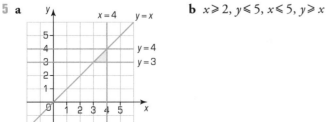

6 a At time 10 minutes   **b** Someone got in the bath.   **c** About 5 minutes

Exercise S1

1 Eddie measured the reflex angle and Steve measured the obtuse angle.

2 $a = 121°$ as $121° + 14° + 45° = 180°$ (and there are 180° in a triangle)

3 Missing angles are 30°, 10° and 38°　　4 $a = 70°$,　$b = 110°$,　$c = 138°$,　$d = 68°$　　5 $x = 145°$,　$y = 35°$

6　　　　EBC = 90° so BCE = 45° (angles in a triangle)

　　　　ABD = 90° so ADB = 28° (angles in a triangle)

　　$x + 28° + 45° = 90°$ (angles in a right angle)

　　　　so $x = 17°$

7 $x = 240°$, $y = 120°$　　8 $x = 65°$

Exercise S2

1 WZ is 8 cm long.　WX is 8 cm long.

The angle at X is equal to the angle at Z.

2 **a** $(4, 2)$　**b** $(0, 3)$　　3 **a** $y = 80°$　**b** $x = 140°$

4 **a** The angles in a triangle add up to 180° and there are three triangles in a pentagon so $3 \times 180° = 540°$

b 720°. The angles in a triangle add up to 180° and there are four triangles in a hexagon so $4 \times 180° = 720°$

c 1440°

5 **a** 135°　**b** 45°　　6 **a** Make all the sides the same length.　**b** Change all the angles to 90°.

7 ABF is equilateral therefore its angles are 60°

CDEF is rectangular therefore its angles are 90°

Angle BFC = 90° − 60° = 30° and angle FBC = 180° − 60° = 120°

Angles in a triangle add up to 180° so angle　BCF = 180° − 120° − 30°

　　　　　　　　　　　　　　　　　　　= 30°

There are two equal angles so BCF is isosceles.

8 **a** 38°　**b** Rhombus　**c** 146°

Exercise S3

1 **a** $x = 40°$　**b** $y = 7.5$ cm　　2 6 cm　　3 **a** $BD^2 = 8^2 + 15^2 = 64 + 225$

　　　　　　　　　　　　　　　　　　　　　　= 289 therefore BD = $\sqrt{289} = 17$

b AD = 18.0278 cm

4 10.9087 cm　　5 11.9583 cm　　6 $25^2 = 625$　$7^2 + 24^2 = 49 + 576 = 625$

The lengths satisfy Pythagoras' theorem so it must be a right-angled triangle.

7 193.132 cm　　8 113.24 cm　　9 2.78 m　　10 800 m

Exercise R3

1 **a** 4　**b** The blue tiles　**c** 1 black, 60 blue　**d** 10　**e** 20

2 **a** $x = 8$　**b** $y = x + 7$　**c** $y = x − 1$　　3 **a** 110°　**b** 50°　　4 **a** A$\hat{B}$D　**b** 50°　**c** $x = 180 − y$　**d** $x = 180 − t − w$

5 **a** They pass each other in opposite directions.　**b** A went past B while B was not moving.　**c** 17.8 km/h

d 28.2 km/h　**e** 13.4 miles/h　　6 7.2 km

Exercise S4

1 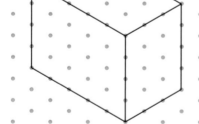　　2

3 **a i** side 3　**ii** side 2　**iii** side 1　**b**

4 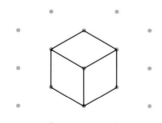　　5

98

Exercise S5

1

2 a Tetrahedron **b** Square-based pyramid

3 a 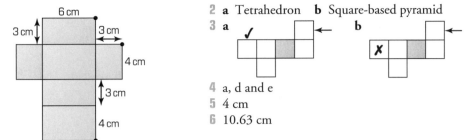 **b**

4 a, d and e
5 4 cm
6 10.63 cm

Exercise S6

1 a Triangle with sides 9 cm, 4 cm and 7 cm **b** Triangle with sides 7 cm, 5 cm and 6 cm

2 a Triangle with all sides 8 cm **b** Three lines of symmetry

3 a Accurate drawing of 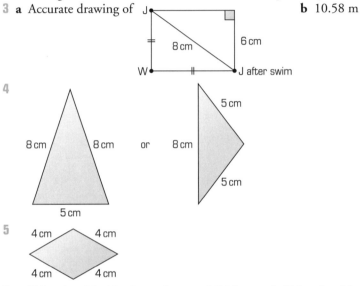 **b** 10.58 m

4

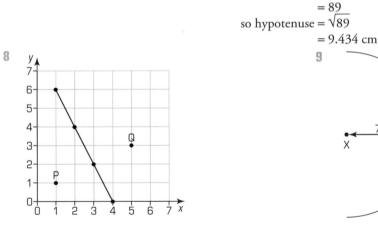

5

6 a Triangle with sides 3 cm, 5 cm and 5.83 cm **b** Triangle with sides 5 cm, 5.83 cm and 5.83 cm

7 a Triangle with sides 5 cm, 8 cm and 9.4 cm **c** $5^2 + 8^2 = 25 + 64$
$$= 89$$
so hypotenuse $= \sqrt{89}$
$$= 9.434 \text{ cm}$$

8

9

Exercise S7

1 a   **b**   **c**

2 a centre of rotation = (0, 0), angle of rotation = 90° anticlockwise **b** (1, 1), (0, ⁻3), (⁻1, ⁻1)

3

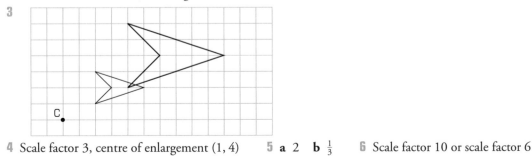

4 Scale factor 3, centre of enlargement (1, 4) **5 a** 2 **b** $\frac{1}{3}$ **6** Scale factor 10 or scale factor 6

Exercise S8

1 **a** 4 bottles **b** 11 2 About 40 inches
3 **a** 54 000 g or 54 kg **b** No. The boxes together weigh 54 kg which is more than the maximum safe amount.
4 450 g raspberries 225 g redcurrants 112 g blackcurrants
  140 g caster sugar 7–8 slices white bread 0.6 litre pudding basin
5 62 mph 6 3.5 hours 7 1140 km 8 5 miles 5 km 5 m 5 feet 5 cm 9 8 kg 8 lb 8 oz 8 g 8 mg
10 2.5 km 11 0.000 288 mm 12 **a** 15 km **b** 8.75 minutes **c** 16.55 km **d** 33.1 km/h

Exercise S9

1 perimeter = 28 cm
2 **a** area = 25 cm^2 **b** 1 cm and 9 cm, 2 cm and 8 cm, 3 cm and 7 cm, 4 cm and 7 cm, 5 cm and 5 cm **c** It is a square.
3 4 cm × 2 cm = 8 cm^2
4 Y X Z
  X: length of side = 24 ÷ 4 = 6 cm
        area = 36 cm^2
  Z: area = 24 × 24
           = 576 cm^2
5 **a** 6 cm **b** 4 cm **c** 9.6 cm
6 **a** 200 cm^2, 60 cm^2, 140 cm^2, 42 cm^2 **b** 442 cm^2. This is equal to the four smaller areas added together.
7 **a** perimeter: 26 cm area: 26 cm^2 **b** perimeter: 40 cm area: 64 cm^2
8 156 m^2 9 4.48 cm

Exercise R4

1

	Number of lines of symmetry			
		0	1	2	3

		0	1	2	3
Order of rotational symmetry	1	E	F		
	2	B		C	
	3	D			A

2 **a** Yes **b** S

3 **a**

4 **a** C **b** 4n + 10 **c** 40 + n **d** 10

5

Exercise S10

1 12 cm 2 108 cm^2
3 A chord is a line connecting two points on a circle. The diameter is the largest chord as the points it connects are as far as possible away from each other.
4 31.83 cm 5 **a** 188.496 cm **b** 121 cm 6 **a** 282.74 cm **b** Twice 7 452.39 cm^2 8 19.1 cm
9 4 cm 10 150.796 cm^2
11   Diameter = 10 cm so radius = 5 cm
   Area of circle = $\pi \times 5^2$ = 78.5
   Area of square = 10 × 10 = 100
      Fraction = $\frac{78.5}{100}$ = 0.785
12 8 people 13 8.17 m^2 14 141.37 cm^2

Exercise S11

1 26 and 22 2 108 cm^2 3 117 cm^2 4 400 5 **a** 56 m^2 **b** 56 000 000 mm^2
6 100 cm or 1 m 7 276.46 cm^2 8 107 cm 9 2 cm, 2 cm and 10 cm

Exercise S12

1 6 cubes 2 72 3 42 cm^3 4 120 cm^3 5 3 cm 6 **a** 4×10^{-8} cm^3 **b** 4×10^{-11} mm^3
7 0.24 m^2 8 **a** 120 cm^3 **b** x = 8 cm 9 113.097 cm^3 10 60 cm^3

Exercise D1

1 **a i** Primary **ii** e.g. will not know what adults think of the chocolate bar
   iii e.g. may be aimed at school children **b** Different people may rate 'a little' and 'a lot' differently.
   c Change 'over 40p' to '40p to 60p' and change 'up to 60p' to 'more than 60p'.
   d

	Yes	A lot	A little	No
Under 40p				
40p to 60p				
Over 60p				

2 **a** Designs 1 and 3 should not be used as they will be difficult to analyse once the results are collected.
   b Design 2 should be used as it is quick and easy to record the results and is easy to analyse.
3 The sample is small and one street may not be representative of a whole area.
4 Ask more than 16 people and ask people who are not her friends/in her year.

Exercise D2

1 e.g. 6 7 11 12   2 e.g. 1 7 10 10 12 14   3 5 or 9   4 5.5 and 8.5   5 290 (10 × 29)
6 6662 or 6671 or 6635   7 4, 4 and 7   8 a 6 b 2   9 a 150 cm b 24 cm   10 13
11 a total tries = (1 × 10) + (1 × 3) + (2 × 4) + (3 × 7) + (4 × 1) = 36 b 2.25
12 a 5 b 5.4 c The mode because it is one of the values.

Exercise R5

1 a Overlap b Various possible answers c Limited age group, for example d Quick and easy, for example
2 a 452 mm² b 226 mm² c 15.0 mm   3 a No b Yes   4 a 300 cm³ b 360 cm³ c 12
5 a 10.6 cm² b 37.2 cm³   6 a 5.72 peas b 1144 c About 36 d $\frac{3}{10}$

Exercise D3

1 a About 60% b

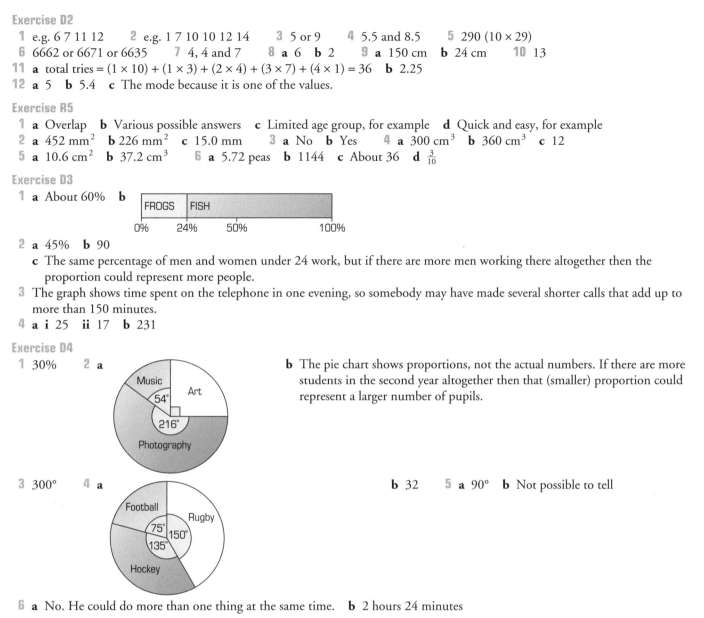

```
┌──────┬──────┬──────────────────────────┐
│FROGS │ FISH │                          │
└──────┴──────┴──────────────────────────┘
0%    24%    50%                      100%
```

2 a 45% b 90
  c The same percentage of men and women under 24 work, but if there are more men working there altogether then the proportion could represent more people.
3 The graph shows time spent on the telephone in one evening, so somebody may have made several shorter calls that add up to more than 150 minutes.
4 a i 25 ii 17 b 231

Exercise D4

1 30%   2 a

b The pie chart shows proportions, not the actual numbers. If there are more students in the second year altogether then that (smaller) proportion could represent a larger number of pupils.

3 300°   4 a

b 32   5 a 90° b Not possible to tell

6 a No. He could do more than one thing at the same time. b 2 hours 24 minutes

Exercise D5

1 a i 11.8 kg ii 10.4 kg b 9 months c

Age (months)	Weight at start, kg	Weight at end, kg	Approximate weight gain, kg
0–6	3.3	7.2	3.9
6–12	7.2	9.6	2.4
12–18	9.6	10.8	1.2
18–24	10.8	12	1.2

2 a Cannot be certain. The graph only shows the trend up to 1998. b False. It fell by exactly $\frac{2}{3}$ from 1500 to 500. c True
3 a i 37.5° ii 38.7° b This can only be an estimate because the temperature is between two readings.

Exercise D6

1 a i Negative correlation ii No relationship b

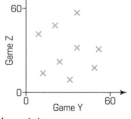

2 a The line of best fit does not have to pass through the origin.
  b The line of best fit should pass as closely as possible to all the points. c Lines of best fit should show the data's trend.
3 a The scatter graph shows that as diameter increases so does height. b
  c Around 10 m
  d This is probably not a pine tree as it does not fit into the trend shown by the line of best fit.
4 a The relationship shown is a negative correlation; as engine capacity increases, urban fuel capacity decreases.
  b i 28 mpg ii 17 mpg c i 1100 cm³ ii 4300 cm³

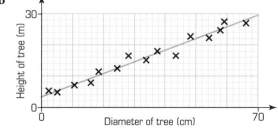

Exercise D7

1 One prime number and one non-prime, e.g. 2 and 4 or 6 and 7   **2 a** Salt and vinegar, or cheese and onion   **b** $\frac{1}{5}$ **c** $\frac{1}{8}$

3 a There are different numbers in each team.   **b** $\frac{5}{23}$ **4 a** p(green) = $\frac{7}{8}$ **b** 7   **c** 14

5 More likely to win as 0.64 is more than 0.5 (equal chances)   **6 a** 0.2   **b** 152 days   **7** 14   **8** 18   **9** 45

Exercise D8

1 $\frac{1}{6}$ **2** TDH THD HTD TDH DHT DTH   **3 a** $\frac{1}{2}$ **b** $\frac{1}{4}$ **4 a** 50p 50p, 50p 20p, 50p 10p, 20p 10p, 20p 20p   **b** $\frac{2}{3}$

5 2285, 2258, 2852, 2582, 2528, 5228, 5282, 5822, 8522, 8252, 8225   **6 a** $\frac{1}{9}$ **b** $\frac{1}{3}$ **c** 0

7 a $\frac{18}{50} = \frac{9}{25}$ **b** $\frac{23}{50}$ **c** $\frac{2}{5}$ **8 a i** 0.35   **ii** 0.35   **b i** 15   **ii** 21

9 a TTT HTT THT TTH THH HTH HHT HHH   **b** 75

Exercise D9

1 a Luke, as he collected the most data.   **b** No, as heads and tails appeared almost equally.   **c** p(tails) = 0.505

2 a Rachel: Purple – 0.59   White – 0.41   Lorna: Purple – 0.44   White – 0.56   **b** Purple – 0.515   White – 0.485

  c The combined results   **d** 5150

3 a $(4 + 6 + 4 + 7 + 6 + 5 + 6 + 4 + 5 + 3 + 3 + 4) \div (10 \times 12) = 0.475$ **b** 200   **4 a** $\frac{1}{32}$ **b** $\frac{15}{32}$

Exercise R6

1 a 20 to 23   **b** 35 to 39   **c** 40 000 to 50 000   **d** B

2 a 30% to 47%   **b** 15% to 24%   **c** angle between 96° and 116° for land

3 a 30%, $\frac{3}{10}$, $\frac{6}{20}$, 0.3   **b i** $\frac{9}{20}$ **ii** 45%   **4 a** Positive correlation   **b** 580 to 595   **c** 166.5 to 167.5

5 a Sue   **b** 0.57   **c** 167, 125, 8   **d** More throws needed   **e** $\frac{1}{1296}$ or 0.000 77

Practice Test Paper 1

1 a Parallel (1)   **b** 2 parallel lines and 1 line crossing them (1)   **2 a** 10th May (1)   **b** 04:36, 19:07 (both 1)

3 a $\frac{1}{24}$ (1)   **b** $\frac{1}{3}$ (1)   **c** $\frac{2}{3}$ (1)   **4** $99 \times 2.5 = £247.50$ (2)

5 a i £160   **ii** £180 (both 1)   **b** £20 (1)   **c** line drawn through (0, 0) and (2, 60) (1)   **d** 2 (1)

6 a

	11		
	12	5	
2	4	1	

(2)   **b** $a = 3$, $b = 5$, $c = 8$ (2)

7 a $\frac{9}{16}$ (1)   **b** $\frac{3}{8}$ (1)   **c** $\frac{3}{16}$ (1)   **8 a** 3, 25 (1)   **b** 12, 8 (1)   **c** Any two of $n - 12$, $\frac{n}{4}$, $\sqrt{n}$ (2)

9 a C, regular shape (both 1)   **b** Same, all 8 (both 1)   **c** 8 (1)   **d** $1 \times 1 \times 12$, $1 \times 2 \times 6$, $1 \times 3 \times 4$, $2 \times 2 \times 3$ (3)

10 a Isosceles (1)   **b** Yes, opposite sides are parallel. (both 1)   **c** No, angles not 90°. (both 1)

11 2nd row: 5, 9 (both 1); 3rd row: ¯4, 7 (both 1)

12 a $\frac{4 \times 3}{9 \times 4} = \frac{1}{3}$ (2)   **b** $\frac{1}{5} \times \frac{2}{3} = \frac{2}{15}$ (1)   **13 a i** $x = y - 7$ **ii** $x = \frac{y}{5}$ **iii** $x = 12y + 6$ (3)   **b** $3 + x = \frac{y}{4}$ $x = \frac{y}{4} - 3$ (2)

14 time = $60 \div 40 = 1.5$ average speed = $48 \div 1.5 = 32$ km/h (2)   **15 a** $(x - 1)(x + 6)$ (1)   **b** $x^2 + 9x + 20$ (2)

16 a Positive (1)   **b** Line drawn through points sloping upwards. (1)   **c** Read from line. (1)   **d** No, not near line. (1)

17 $\frac{10}{16}$ (2)   **18** orange $\frac{15}{16}$, lime $\frac{5}{16}$, lemonade $1\frac{1}{4}$ (3)   **19** Two sides add to 7: $1 + 6$, $2 + 5$, $3 + 4$ (3)

Practice Test Paper 2

1

(2)   **2 a** 18 °C (1)   **b** Bar drawn from 2 to 13 (2)

3 a No, total not 360 (both 1)   **b** $360 - (90 + 55 + 65) = 150$ (2)

4 a 24 divisible by 2, 3, 4, … (1)   **b** 4 not prime and all other numbers will be divisible by 4. (1)

  c 5 is prime; multiples of 5 cannot be. (1)

5 24 (1)   **6 a** Drawing of parallelogram (rectangle) not rhombus or square (1)   **b** Drawing of kite (1)

7 $(350 - 32) \times \frac{5}{9}$ or $(360 - 32) \times \frac{5}{9}$, 180, yes (3)   **8 a** 12 (1)   **b** $\frac{1}{2} \times 4 \times h = 4 \times 4$, $h = 8$ (2)

9 0.23×3765, £865.95 (2)   **b** $\frac{1280}{3765} \times 100$, 34% (2)

10 a Any three of: (0, 5) (1, 4) (2, 3) (3, 2) (4, 1) (5, 0) (1)   **b** $x + y = 5$ (1)   **c** Line $x + y = 2$ drawn (1)

11 a max 36, min ¯24 (both 1)   **b** $(4 \times 3) + (6 \times \,^-2) = 0$ (1)

  c 2 answered, all correct; 7 answered, 4 correct, 3 incorrect; 12 answered, 6 correct, 6 incorrect (2)

12 a 78.5 cm² (1)   **b** $550 \div 78.5 = 7$ cm (2)   **13 a** $\frac{9}{21} = \frac{3}{7}$ (2)   **b** $2\frac{1}{2} \div 7\frac{1}{2} = \frac{1}{3}$ (2)

14 a $4 \times 4 = 16$ (2)   **b** $\frac{6}{32} \times 360 = 67.5°$ (2)   **15 a** yellow 160 ml, blue 40 ml (both 1)   **b** red 7.5 ml, blue 2.5 ml (2)

16 $8 \times 44 - (3 \times 43 + 2 \times 44 + 45 + 48) = 42$ (2)

17 a sum interior angles $7 \times 180°$; interior angle $1260 \div 9 = 140°$ (1)   **b** 100° (1)

18 a 12 (1)   **b** 20 (1)   **c** 6 (1)   **19** 1 and ¯1 (2)   **20** $12.8^2 + 10.4^2 \neq 17.2^2$, no (2)   **21** $3x = 12$, $x = 4$ (2)